DATE DUE			
FEB 21 '89'S			
OCT 0 1 1997			
ILL 6773916 KQU			
WITHDRAWN			

Computer Modelling
in Electrostatics

ELECTRONIC & ELECTRICAL ENGINEERING RESEARCH STUDIES

ELECTROSTATICS AND ELECTROSTATIC APPLICATIONS SERIES

Series Editor: **Dr J. F. Hughes,** *Department of Electrical Engineering, University of Southampton, England*

Computer Modelling in Electrostatics

D. McAllister
University of Aberdeen, Scotland

J. R. Smith
University of Aberdeen, Scotland

and

N. J. Diserens
Rutherford Appleton Laboratory, England

RESEARCH STUDIES PRESS LTD.
Letchworth, Hertfordshire, England
JOHN WILEY & SONS INC.
New York · Chichester · Toronto · Brisbane · Singapore

RESEARCH STUDIES PRESS LTD.
58B Station Road, Letchworth, Herts. SG6 3BE, England

Marketing and Distribution:

Australia, New Zealand, South-east Asia:
Jacaranda-Wiley Ltd., Jacaranda Press
JOHN WILEY & SONS INC.
GPO Box 859, Brisbane, Queensland 4001, Australia

Canada:
JOHN WILEY & SONS CANADA LIMITED
22 Worcester Road, Rexdale, Ontario, Canada

Europe, Africa:
JOHN WILEY & SONS LIMITED
Baffins Lane, Chichester, West Sussex, England

North and South America and the rest of the world:
JOHN WILEY & SONS INC.
605 Third Avenue, New York, NY 10158, USA

Library of Congress Cataloging in Publication Data:

McAllister, D.
  Computer modelling in electrostatics.

  (Electronic & electrical engineering research studies. Electrostatics and electrostatic applications series; 6)
  Bibliography: p.
  Includes index.
  1. Electrostatic apparatus and appliances—Mathematical models.   2. Electrostatic apparatus and appliances—Data processing.   I. Smith, J. R. (John Robert), 1937–
II. Diserens, N. J.   III. Title.   IV. Series.
QC573.M34   1985   537'.2   85-14479

ISBN 0 86380 035 1
ISBN 0 471 90882 7 (Wiley)

British Library Cataloguing in Publication Data:

McAllister, D.
  Computer modelling in electrostatics.—(Electronic & electrical engineering research studies. Electrostatics and electrostatic applications series; 6)
  1. Electrostatics—Data processing
  2. Electrostatics—Mathematical models
  I. Title   II. Smith, J. R.   III. Diserens, N. J.
IV. Series.
621.31'26   TK153

ISBN 0 86380 035 1
ISBN 0 471 90882 7 Wiley

ISBN 0 86380 035 1 (Research Studies Press Ltd.)
ISBN 0 471 90882 7 (John Wiley & Sons Inc.)

Printed in Great Britain

Contents

Editorial Foreword

The use of computer modelling techniques as an aid to engineering design has seen dramatic developments in recent years, and there are currently no indications that the rapid growth and sophistication of such techniques are likely to plateau in the near future. In a concise and easy to read volume, the authors have brought together fundamental considerations and experimental applications of modelling in one specific branch of engineering - electrostatics.

The basic equations are introduced and followed by a brief explanation of solution method. The practical examples used to illustrate the modelling methods are especially useful. These are not hypothetical situations, but real experimental case studies showing the step-by-step approach to modelling of both large and small scale systems.

As well as being an extremely useful manual for the industrial electrostatics engineer, this volume complements the other titles in this series on Electrostatics and Electrostatic Applications.

Dr. J.F. Hughes,
Ph.D., M.I.E.E., F.Inst.P.

April 1985

Principal Symbols

D	dielectric displacement
E	electrostatic field
F	Faraday number
i,j,k,l,m,n	nodal indices
I_s	streaming current
m	mass
N_i	shape functions
Q	charge
R	gas constant
S	Schmidt number
s	electrokinetic potential
T	temperature
K	electrical conductivity
v	velocity
$x,y,z,$	cartesian coordinates
W	energy
r,θ,z	polar coordinates
ε_o	permittivity of free space
ε_r	relative permittivity
η	viscosity
μ	transference number
Δp	pressure drop
ρ	space charge density
σ	surface charge

τ	torque
ϕ	electrostatic potential
∇	differential operator
ξ,η,ρ	normalised coordinates

CHAPTER 1
Introduction

The aims of this book are to present mathematical methods and
derived numerical techniques for investigating the behaviour and
application of electrostatic fields. The subject is of importance to
physicists and practising engineers because of the many practical and
industrial situations where electrostatic effects are involved.

In many industrial applications charged particles may be used in a
variety of ways, to perform useful functions when interacting with
electrostatic fields. As early as 1824 Hohlfeld of Leipzig demon-
strated experimentally that solid particles or liquid droplets could
be removed from the gas in which they were suspended. Subsequent
development of the electrostatic filter or precipitator has resulted
in plant capable of handling large volumes of gas at high tempera-
tures if required, with equipment of moderate size and with only
small drops in pressure across the unit. Similar development has
led to electrostatic forces being used to separate or sort mixed
particulate industrial materials. Electrostatic paint spraying and
xerography are further examples of the beneficial uses which this
interaction makes possible.

In contrast, the undesirable effects of random, and sometimes
uncontrolled, charging of a material in certain circumstances may
lead to a hazardous condition. The generation of static electricity
during the transport of low conductivity materials is a well known
phenomenon. Until recently, large-scale experimentation has been
the principal means by which the electrostatic conditions associated

with the charging process have been assessed. Furthermore, the wide range of materials which exhibit differing charging characteristics, together with the various sizes of containers in common use, make conclusions drawn from one arrangement difficult to apply to others. Consequently, there is an increasing need, at the initial stage of industrial storage facility design, to assess the effect of the electrostatic conditions arising from the transport of these materials. Engineers are at present in need of more information about the mechanism of charging in typical fluid and powder storage installations. In this book some attention is given to this parti-cular problem by carrying out experimentation and using a computer solution in a pseudo interactive manner to further the understanding of the charging and relaxation mechanisms and to assist generally in the forward design of storage facilities.

The book is concerned with achieving the dual objective of presenting a clear exposition of practical electrostatic problems and their solution by numerical techniques which are simply explained strictly in terms of the subject matter. The mathematical problem that presents itself is the solution of Poisson's equation. Although this governing equation is common in many branches of science, its analytical solution for all but the simplest geometries is usually impossible to achieve. The increasing availability of large computer facilities has, however, made the numerical solution of such problems a viable proposition. In consequence, the text is liberally illustrated by examples which assist in the understanding of the development of the text as it progresses. Chapters 6 and 7 are essentially case studies concerning the transport of low conductivity fluids and powders and represent the use of the analysis in hazard evaluation. In addition, appendices giving necessary mathematical formulae and a simple computer program suitable for the solution of axisymmetric problems are included to assist the reader to take the first steps towards solving relatively simple problems.

Numerical techniques by their nature often require specialised knowledge in order to utilise them from first principles. Many who would gain much from their use find the mathematical way in which they are presented prohibitive. In trying to present a document which is easily read, certain features of this text may be more precisely or elegantly expressed in complex mathematical jargon. It has however, been the intention from the onset to provide an introductory text on numerical methods specifically related to electrostatics leaving the reader to delve further, if required, into more advanced numerical techniques.

CHAPTER 2
Theoretical Background

INTRODUCTION

The theoretical background which is necessary to enable a good understanding of electrostatic field analysis is readily derived from a
few simple relationships. We shall start by considering the effect
of point charges and develop the analysis to consider surface and
volume charge.

2.1 POINT CHARGE

The expression for field due to an isolated point charge located in
an infinite space is:

$$\bar{E} = \frac{Q}{4\pi\varepsilon_o r^2} \cdot \hat{r} \tag{2.1}$$

In other words, the field due to a point charge is directed radially
outwards and is inversely proportional to the square of the distance
from the source. Using the relationship

$$\bar{E} = -\nabla\phi$$

$$= -(\frac{\partial\phi}{\partial x} \cdot \hat{i} + \frac{\partial\phi}{\partial y} \cdot \hat{j} + \frac{\partial\phi}{\partial z} \cdot \hat{k}) \tag{2.2}$$

the expression:

$$\phi = \frac{Q}{4\pi\varepsilon_o r} \tag{2.3}$$

can be derived for the potential at a point r distant from a single
point charge. Equation (2.3) although simple, does not readily lend
itself to expansion for more complex charge distributions.

If we consider a point charge located in the coordinate system
shown in figure 2.1, a more convenient expression for potential due
to a point charge is:

$$\phi(\bar{r}) = \frac{1}{4\pi\epsilon_0} \frac{Q}{|\bar{r} - \bar{r}'|} \qquad (2.4)$$

(Note for $\bar{r}' = 0$ equation 2.4 is identical to 2.3)

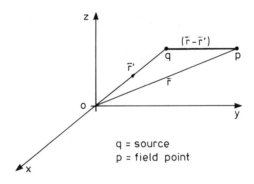

q = source
p = field point

Figure 2.1   Point charge

It is worth noting that neither the potential nor the field at a
point source is defined since the expressions for field and potential
tend to infinity as $|\bar{r} - \bar{r}'|$ tends to 0.

2.2 SURFACE CHARGE

An expression for field due to a surface charge on a conductor may
be derived from the expression for field due to a point charge. First
we shall derive the expression for field on the axis of a conducting
ring. Consider the arrangement shown in figure 2.2. An isolated
conducting ring of radius R carries a charge of Q coulombs. As the
ring is conducting and symmetrical it may be assumed that the charge

6

is evenly distributed. A small section of ring, δL, positioned at p
carries a charge

$$\delta Q = \frac{Q}{2\pi R} \, \delta L \qquad\qquad (2.5)$$

This section of charged ring contributes $\delta \bar{E}_2$ to the field at 0 where:

$$\delta \bar{E}_2 = \frac{\delta Q}{4\pi \varepsilon_o r_2} \, \hat{r}$$

$$= \frac{Q \, \delta L}{\delta \pi^2 \varepsilon_o R r^2} \, \hat{r}_2 \qquad\qquad (2.6)$$

Similarly the elemental section δL at P' will contribute $\delta \bar{E}_1$ at 0.

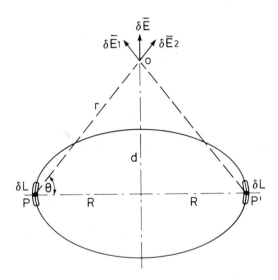

Figure 2.2   Conducting ring

Adding the two contributions will yield

$$\delta \bar{E} = \delta \bar{E}_1 + \delta \bar{E}_2$$

where

$$\delta\bar{E} = 2\delta\bar{E}_1 \frac{d}{r} \qquad\qquad (\sin\,\theta = \frac{d}{r})$$

i.e.

$$\delta\bar{E} = \frac{Qd\delta L}{4\pi^2\varepsilon_0 Rr^3} \cdot \hat{r} \qquad\qquad (2.7)$$

The total field strength at 0 may now be found by integrating around the ring.

$$\bar{E} = \frac{Q\,d}{4\pi^2\varepsilon_0 r^3 R}\ \hat{r}\int_{0}^{\pi R} dL$$

$$= \frac{Q\,d}{4\pi\varepsilon_0 r^3} \cdot \hat{r} \qquad\qquad (\text{Note:}\quad r = \sqrt{d^2 + R^2})$$

$$= \frac{Q\,d}{4\pi\varepsilon_0 (d^2 + R^2)^{3/2}} \qquad\qquad (2.8)$$

Having derived an expression for field on the axis of a charged ring, we may now proceed to use this relationship to determine the field due to a uniformly charged infinite plane.

Consider the arrangement shown in figure 2.3. A plane with charge distribution ρ_s [Cm^{-2}] extends to infinity. The charge contained on an elemental annulus of radius R and thickness δR is

$$\delta Q = 2\pi\rho_s R\delta R \qquad\qquad (2.9)$$

Using the relationship derived for a charged ring the field vertically above the ring is

$$\delta\bar{E} = \frac{\delta Qd}{4\pi\varepsilon_0 (R^2 + d^2)^{3/2}} \cdot \hat{r}$$

$$= \frac{\rho_s d}{2\varepsilon_0}\ \frac{R\delta R}{(R^2 + d^2)^{3/2}} \qquad\qquad (2.10)$$

By integrating over the total region the field due to the charged infinite plane is:

$$|\bar{E}| = \frac{d\rho_s}{2\varepsilon_o} \int\limits_0^\infty \frac{RdR}{(R^2 + d^2)^{3/2}}$$

$$= \frac{\rho_s}{2\varepsilon_o} \qquad (2.11)$$

directed normal to the plane.

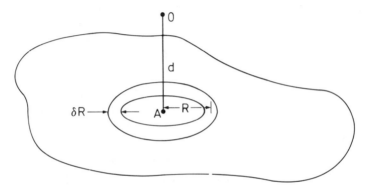

Figure 2.3   Surface charge

As in the case of a point charge this expression although simple is inconvenient for use in more general terms (e.g. non-infinite plane). By positioning a charged plane in the coordinate system as shown in Figure 2.4, a more suitable form of this relationship may be derived. The potential at a field point due to a small element of area $\delta s'$ containing charge $\rho_s \delta s'$ is

$$\delta\phi = \frac{1}{4\pi\varepsilon_o} \frac{\rho_s \delta s'}{|\bar{r} - \bar{r}'|} \qquad (2.12)$$

By dividing the charged plane into a large number of small elemental areas and adding the potential contributions from each we obtain

$$\phi(\bar{r}) = \frac{1}{4\pi\varepsilon_o} \int_s \frac{\rho_s \, ds'}{|\bar{r} - \bar{r}'|} \qquad (2.13)$$

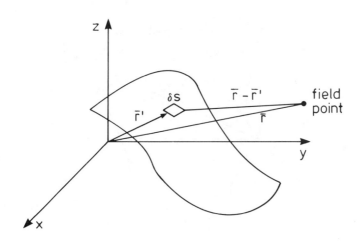

Figure 2.4   Charged plane

2.3   VOLUME CHARGE

Although analytical expressions for the field due to certain volume charge distributions may be readily derived, we shall not do so in this discussion. We shall proceed directly to a general expression for potential due to a defined volume charge distribution. Consider a small volume $\delta v'$ containing a charge density ρ as shown in figure 2.5. The potential at a field point due to this elemental charged volume is:

$$\delta\phi = \frac{1}{4\pi\varepsilon_o} \frac{\rho\delta v'}{|\bar{r} - \bar{r}'|} \qquad (2.14)$$

By subdividing the region of interest into a large number of such elements and adding the contribution from each we obtain an expression for potential at a field point due to a volume charge distribution

$$\phi(\bar{r}) = \frac{1}{4\pi\epsilon_0} \int_V \frac{\rho(\bar{r}') \, dv'}{|\bar{r} - \bar{r}'|} \tag{2.15}$$

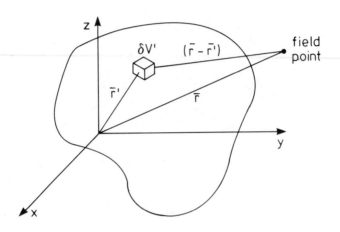

Figure 2.5   Volume charge

2.4 DIELECTRIC BOUNDARIES

So far we have considered charges in free space. In practical problems one frequently encounters different dielectric media having different dielectric constants. A change in dielectric constant from one region to another has the effect of introducing a discontinuity in the electric field as shown in figure 2.6.

By defining the dielectric displacement

$$\bar{D} = \epsilon\bar{E}$$

then

$$\bar{D}_{1N} = \bar{D}_{2N}$$

i.e. $\quad \varepsilon_1 \bar{E}_{1N} = \varepsilon_2 \bar{E}_{2N}$

and $\quad \bar{E}_{2T} = \bar{E}_{1T}$ $\hspace{4cm}$ (2.16)

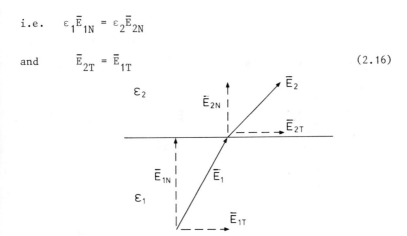

Figure 2.6 $\quad$ Discontinuity due to a dielectric boundary

Returning to the result in equation 2.4 for the field due to a surface charge on an infinite conductor. If we now assume that dielectric constant above the plane is ε_{1r} and below is ε_{2r} (see figure 2.7) then $\bar{E}_{1N}$ and $\bar{E}_{2N}$ can be expressed as

$$\bar{E}_{1N} = - \frac{\rho_s}{2\varepsilon_o \varepsilon_{1r}} \cdot \hat{n}$$

$$\bar{E}_{2N} = \frac{\rho_s}{2\varepsilon_o \varepsilon_{2r}} \cdot \hat{n}$$

i.e.

$$\varepsilon_{2r} \bar{E}_{2N} - \varepsilon_{1r} \bar{E}_{1N} = \frac{\rho_s}{\varepsilon_o} \cdot \hat{n} \hspace{3cm} (2.17)$$

or

$$\bar{D}_{2N} - \bar{D}_{1N} = \frac{\rho_s}{\varepsilon_o} \cdot \hat{n}$$

12

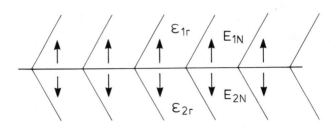

Figure 2.7   Dielectric boundary

2.5 POISSON'S AND LAPLACE'S EQUATIONS

Poisson's equation may quite readily be derived from Gauss's Law:

$$\nabla \cdot (\varepsilon_r \bar{E}) = \frac{\rho}{\varepsilon_o} \tag{2.18}$$

and

$$\bar{E} = -\nabla \phi \tag{2.19}$$

Substituting for $\bar{E}$ yields

$$\nabla \cdot (\varepsilon_r \nabla \phi) = -\frac{\rho}{\varepsilon_o} \tag{2.20}$$

For homogeneous media (ε_r constant)

$$\nabla^2 \phi = -\frac{\rho}{\varepsilon_o \varepsilon_r} \qquad \text{--- Poisson's equation} \tag{2.21}$$

In a region containing no charge this simplifies to

$$\nabla^2 \phi = 0 \qquad \text{--- Laplace's equation} \tag{2.22}$$

In cartesian coordinates (2.21) becomes

$$\frac{\partial^2 \phi}{\partial x^2} + \frac{\partial^2 \phi}{\partial y^2} + \frac{\partial^2 \phi}{\partial z^2} = -\frac{\rho}{\varepsilon_o \varepsilon_r} \tag{2.23}$$

If there is no variation of potential in one of the coordinate directions, say the z direction, (2.23) becomes

$$\frac{\partial^2 \phi}{\partial x^2} + \frac{\partial^2 \phi}{\partial y^2} = - \frac{\rho}{\varepsilon_o \varepsilon_r} \qquad (2.24)$$

Re-expressing (2.23) in cylindrical coordinates r, z, θ
i.e.

yields

$$\frac{1}{r} \left(\frac{\partial}{\partial r} \left(r \frac{\partial \phi}{\partial r} \right) \right) + \frac{1}{r^2} \frac{\partial^2 \phi}{\partial \theta^2} + \frac{\partial^2 \phi}{\partial z^2} = - \frac{\rho}{\varepsilon_o \varepsilon_r} \qquad (2.25)$$

if the problem is axisymmetric, that is ϕ is independent of rotation
then (2.25) becomes

$$\frac{1}{r} \left(\frac{\partial}{\partial r} \left(r \frac{\partial \phi}{\partial r} \right) \right) + \frac{\partial^2 \phi}{\partial z^2} = - \frac{\rho}{\varepsilon_o \varepsilon_r} \qquad (2.26)$$

For all problems equation (2.23) is true. For problems which may be
considered infinite in one coordinate direction, the simpler equation
(2.24) may be used while for axisymmetric problems (2.26) is a simple
version.

It may be readily shown that the equations which we have derived
for potential due to volume (2.15), surface (2.13) and point charges
($r \neq 0$) (2.4) all satisfy both Poisson's and Laplace's equations.
The three expressions for volume, surface and point charge fields may
be used to derive a solution for 'free space' potential given a charge
distribution. This implies that no boundary conditions are imposed.
On the other hand we have stated that these expressions satisfy
Poisson's equation. Assuming that the physical problem which we are
interested in can be posed in terms of charge distribution and
material properties, then a solution of Poisson's equation subject
to the appropriate boundary conditions is precisely what we seek –
the solution to our field problem.

Consider a closed surface S bounding a volume V; the following
types of boundary can exist. The value of potential ϕ is specified
everywhere on the boundary S. This is known as a DIRICHLET boundary
condition.

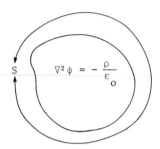

$\phi = g(s)$ (prescribed) on S

Figure 2.8

The value of $\frac{\partial \phi}{\partial n}$, the normal derivative of ϕ, is specified over the
whole surface S. This is known as a NEUMANN boundary condition and
may be thought of as equal to a surface charge imposed on the
boundary.

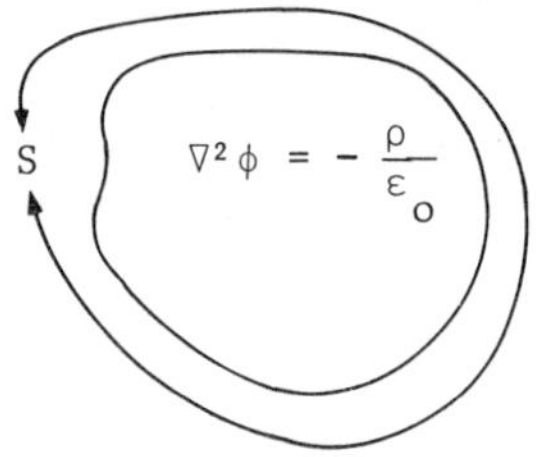

$\frac{\partial \phi}{\partial n} = h(s)$ (prescribed) on S

Figure 2.9

The value of ϕ is specified on part of the boundary and $\frac{\partial \phi}{\partial n}$ is
specified on the remainder

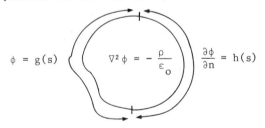

$\phi = g(s)$ $\frac{\partial \phi}{\partial n} = h(s)$

Figure 2.10

2.6   ENERGY IN AN ELECTROSTATIC FIELD

The electrostatic energy in a region may be thought of as being made up from two separate parts - the energy associated with any charge in the region and the energy associated with the field in the regions due to external charges.

Just as the energy stored in a capacitor may be expressed as:

$$W = \tfrac{1}{2} Q \phi$$

so the energy in a volume δV, due to charge in that volume may be expressed as

$$\delta W = \tfrac{1}{2} \rho \phi \delta V$$

Similarly the energy in a volume due to external charges is dependent on the field which is generated by those charges, i.e.

$$\delta W = \tfrac{1}{2} \varepsilon_o \varepsilon_r \bar{E}^2 \ . \ \delta V$$

Combining the two contributions gives the total electrostatic energy in a small volume δV as

$$\delta W = (\tfrac{1}{2} \varepsilon_o \varepsilon_r \bar{E}^2 + \tfrac{1}{2} \rho \phi) \delta V$$

The total energy in a general region V bounded by a surface S is

$$W = \int_v (\tfrac{1}{2} \varepsilon_o \varepsilon_r \bar{E}^2 + \tfrac{1}{2} \rho \phi) \delta V + \int_s \tfrac{1}{2} \rho_s \phi \ . \ ds$$

2.7   SUMMARY

To summarise, the potential distribution due to a point, surface or volume charge distributions in 'free space' are as follows:

$$\text{Point} \qquad \phi(\bar{r}) = \frac{1}{4\pi\varepsilon_o} \ \frac{Q}{|\bar{r} - \bar{r}'|}$$

Surface $\qquad \phi(\bar{r}) = \dfrac{1}{4\pi\varepsilon_o} \displaystyle\int_s \dfrac{\rho_s}{|\bar{r} - \bar{r}'|} \, ds'$

Volume $\qquad \phi(\bar{r}) = \dfrac{1}{4\pi\varepsilon_o} \displaystyle\int_v \dfrac{\rho_s}{|\bar{r} - \bar{r}'|} \, dv'$

For electrostatic problems simply involving such distributions of charge with no boundary surfaces the above expressions provide a simple and convenient solution to the 'free space' potential distribution.

On the other hand, for problems involving boundary conditions such as fixed potentials or surface charge layers, solution of Poisson's equation provides the appropriate potential solution: i.e.

$$\nabla(\varepsilon_r \, \nabla.\phi) = -\dfrac{\rho}{\varepsilon_o}$$

subject to the relevant boundary conditions

$\phi(s) = g(s)$ $\qquad\qquad\qquad$ fixed potential

$\dfrac{\partial\phi}{\partial n}(s) = h(s)$ $\qquad\qquad\qquad$ surface charge.

At dielectric boundaries tangential $\bar{E}$ and normal $\bar{D}$ are conserved. The electrostatic energy in a region can be expressed as

$$W = \int_v (\tfrac{1}{2}\,\varepsilon_r\varepsilon_o\,\bar{E}^2 + \tfrac{1}{2}\,\rho\,\phi).\,dv + \int_s \tfrac{1}{2}\,\rho_s\,\phi\,.\,ds.$$

CHAPTER 3
Differential Methods

INTRODUCTION

In this chapter attention is directed towards seeking the solution
of Poisson's equation in a finite region bounded by a closed curve
on which a boundary condition is specified at every point. This is
the most frequently encountered type of problem in practical electrostatics. The differential methods that are discussed in the following are those which solve the equation by effectively integrating
over the whole of the bounded problem to be investigated. The
solution for electrostatic potential or field is first obtained over
a mesh of points called nodes. By using numerical techniques,
potentials and fields can then be obtained at any other defined
point in the model. The two techniques that are commonly used are
the Finite Difference and Finite Element methods.

The accuracy of the solution will depend on the fineness of the
mesh. In most Finite Difference computer programs the mesh is
regularly spaced and additional refinement implies the inclusion of
more mesh points even in areas where this is not necessary to improve
accuracy. In the Finite Element method the mesh size can vary over
the model thus enabling the user to put a finer spacing in regions
where the gradient of the potential function is subject to rapid
change. The user will thus be able to obtain optimum accuracy for
minimum total mesh. An alternative method for refining the solution
is to use initially a coarse mesh and to 'zoom in' on areas where
the fields are to be more accurately computed. A new boundary is

18

drawn around the expanded area, taking care that these boundary
points are not themselves critical, and then a new model is set up
with a finer mesh to cover the region of interest, using the
potentials from the first run on the new boundary.

3.1   FINITE DIFFERENCE METHOD

This method, Allen (1954), Carre (1961) and Forsythe and Wasow
(1960), has been traditionally used for solving field problems with
two dimensional or axisymmetric geometry and was pioneered by
Southwell (1946) long before the advent of modern computers.   In its
simplest application a regular 'net' is imposed over the problem as
shown in figure 3.1.

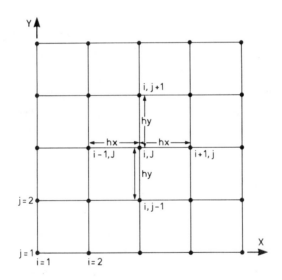

Figure 3.1   Finite difference mesh

The nodal points at which a solution will be obtained are the
intersection of the mesh lines.   The first stage in considering a
solution method is to derive a relationship between a node and its
four closest neighbours.   Suppose that the potential at node (i,j) is
$\phi_{i,j}$.   By Taylor's Theorem, if the spacing between node (i,j)

and the next node (i+1, j) in the 'x' direction is hx, then $\phi_{i+1,j}$ may be expressed as the infinite series:

$$\phi_{i+1,j} = \phi_{i,j} + \frac{1}{1!}\frac{\partial\phi}{\partial x}hx + \frac{1}{2!}\frac{\partial^2\phi}{\partial x^2}h_x^2 + \ldots \text{ etc.} \qquad (3.1)$$

where the derivatives are those at node (i,j).

Similarly, for node (i-1, j) on the negative x side of node (i,j),

$$\phi_{i-1,j} = \phi_{i,j} - \frac{1}{1!}\frac{\partial\phi}{\partial x}h_x + \frac{1}{2!}\frac{\partial^2\phi}{\partial x^2}h_x^2 - \ldots \text{ etc.} \qquad (3.2)$$

Adding these two equations gives:

$$\phi_{i+1,j} + \phi_{i-1,j} = 2\phi_{i,j} + \frac{\partial^2\phi}{\partial x^2}h_x^2 + e \qquad (3.3)$$

where 'e' represents a small correction comprising the higher even order terms and can be made as small as desired by making hx small enough. (It should be noted that the smaller the spacing the longer the running time on a computer and the more store it will need). Thus

$$\frac{\partial^2\phi}{\partial x^2} = \frac{\phi_{i+1,j} + \phi_{i-1,j} - 2\phi_{i,j}}{h_x^2} \qquad (3.4)$$

is approximately true.

Similarly, if the spacing in the y direction is hy:

$$\frac{\partial^2\phi}{\partial y^2} = \frac{\phi_{i,j+1} + \phi_{i,j-1} - 2\phi_{i,j}}{h_y^2} \qquad (3.5)$$

Adding these two equations we now find that:

$$\nabla^2\phi = \frac{\phi_{i+1,j} + \phi_{i-1,j} - 2\phi_{i,j}}{h_x^2} + \frac{\phi_{i,j+1} + \phi_{i,j-1} - 2\phi_{i,j}}{h_y^2}$$

$$= \frac{-\rho}{\varepsilon_o\varepsilon_r} \qquad (3.6)$$

where ρ is the charge density at node (i,j).

Or, if hx = hy = h (i.e. the mesh spacing is the same in both coordinate directions):

$$\phi_{i,j} = \frac{1}{4} \left(\phi_{i+1,j} + \phi_{i,j+1} + \phi_{i-1,j} + \phi_{i,j-1} + \frac{h^2 \rho}{\varepsilon_o \varepsilon_r} \right) \qquad (3.7)$$

In the model shown in figure 3.2 the boundary nodes will already have potentials assigned to them. Other internal nodes are usually set initially at zero and a table is made of all nodal potentials.

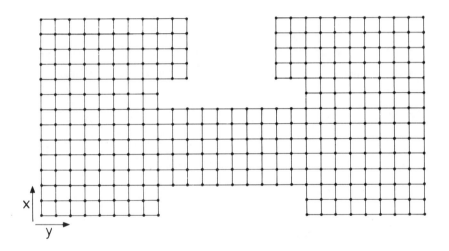

Figure 3.2   Finite difference mesh for switch contactor

The mesh is now scanned sequentially, updating the tabulated value of the potential at each point according to equation 3.6. The scan should take place mesh line by mesh line, either horizontally or vertically. Some authors prefer to scan alternate lines forward and backwards. After a number of scans depending on the particular problem and also the number of mesh points, the potential values should settle down to the required solution. In the computer program the process is refined by over-relaxation. That is, applying a greater adjustment than indicated by the equation so that convergence is speeded up, or perhaps at times a smaller adjustment to prevent oscillation. Carre's Method (1961) is one scheme which is widely used. The 'difference equation' (Equation 3.6) must be modified where the node lies close to a sloping boundary, on a dielectric interface or on a plane of symmetry where only one side is represented in the model.

To compute the potential and field components at any point a crude answer can be obtained as follows.

Consider the mesh rectangle bounded by nodes (i,j), $(i,j+1)$, $(i+1, j+1)$, $(i+1,j)$ shown in figure 3.3

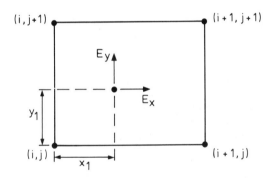

Figure 3.3   Finite difference mesh rectangle

Now suppose we desire to find the field components and potential at a point in the rectangle at a distance x_1 in the x direction and y_1 in the y direction from (i,j). We require the negative of the potential gradient.

The mean value of E_{xB} along the bottom edge of the rectangle is

$$E_{xB} = \frac{\phi_{i,j} - \phi_{i+1,j}}{h_x}$$

and the mean value of E_{xT} along the top edge of the rectangle is

$$E_{xT} = \frac{\phi_{i,j+1} - \phi_{i+1,j+1}}{h_x}$$

So, by interpolation, an estimate of E_x at the field point will be:

$$E_x = \frac{1}{h_x h_y} [(\phi_{i,j} - \phi_{i+1,j})(h_y - y_1) + y_1(\phi_{i,j+1} - \phi_{i+1,j+1})]$$

$$(3.8)$$

Similarly, an estimate of E_y is given by:

$$E_y = \frac{1}{h_x h_y} [(\phi_{i,j} - \phi_{i,j+1})(h_x - x_1) + x_1(\phi_{i+1,j} - \phi_{i+1,j+1})$$

$$(3.9)$$

for potential values, at a distance x_1 along the bottom edge:

$$\phi_b = \frac{x_1}{h_x} (\phi_{i+1,j} - \phi_{i,j}) + \phi_{i,j}$$

$$(3.10)$$

Similarly, at a distance x_1 along the top edge:

$$\phi_t = \frac{x_1}{h_x} (\phi_{i+1,j+1} - \phi_{i,j+1}) + \phi_{i,j+1}$$

$$(3.11)$$

Therefore an estimate for the value at the field point is:

$$\phi_p = \frac{y_1}{h_y} (\phi_t - \phi_b) + \phi_b$$

$$(3.12)$$

This will give fairly smooth values of potential, but plots of
electric field will appear discontinuous. Formulae which involve
a 'spline' fit using more nodal potential values are needed to
produce smooth results. If this is done, however, care must be
taken near dielectric interfaces to see that correct continuity
conditions are maintained (i.e. normal D and tangential E must
be continuous across the dielectric boundary). (See section 2.4).

Use of the finite difference method to solve three dimensional
problems is possible, but the large numbers of nodes which are

required make it generally uneconomic to use with a regular mesh. Computer programs which have a variable mesh size are generally equivalent to Finite Element programs. The chief difference is that the latter tend to employ direct matrix solution methods rather than the relaxation technique described above.

3.2 FINITE ELEMENT METHOD

This method, (Hinton and Owen (1979), Zienkiewicz (1977)), was first developed for structural analysis and was later applied to electromagnetic field problems. It can be used for solving problems in two or three dimensions or those which are relatively symmetric The model under investigation is regarded as being divided into elements. For field problems in two dimensions, elements are generally triangles or rectangles. The sides of the elements may if necessary be curved. Three dimensional elements are often brick shaped but here again there are generally available several element types from which to choose. Figure 3.4 illustrates some of the more common shapes for both two and three dimensions. Figure 3.5 shows a typical finite element model of the switch contact shown in Figure 3.2. However, in this case the mesh is triangular and need not be regular.

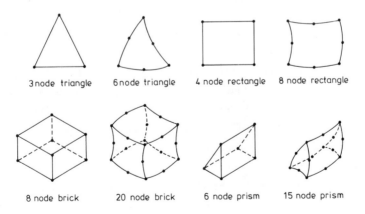

3 node triangle   6 node triangle   4 node rectangle   8 node rectangle

8 node brick   20 node brick   6 node prism   15 node prism

Figure 3.4   A selection of element shapes

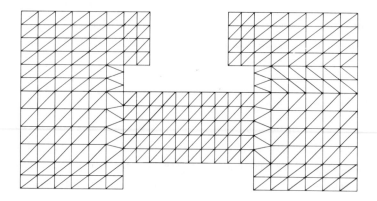

Figure 3.5   Finite element discretization of switch
contactor problem

Three dimensional finite element models are frequently displayed as
sections through individual planes through the mesh. Graphical
portrayal of the 3D discretisation tends to produce an unintelligible
picture. Views of dielectric surfaces or electrodes are sometimes
shown, with the outlines of the element faces which touch them. These
look similar to two dimensional meshes.

The potential solution, as in the Finite Difference method, will
first be obtained at a number of predefined points (nodes) within
the model. There will be a node at each vertex of each element. If
the element sides are to be regarded as curved there will also be at
least one intermediate node on each side. Although it is possible
to mix elements with different topological shapes and different
numbers of nodes it is fairly common for the elements used to be all
of the same kind. Nodes on an interface between two elements must
normally be part of the topology of both adjoining elements. Most
types of element have all their nodes on their outer surface as
this gives economy of total numbers of nodes and therefore of the
number of equations to be solved. Also if the potential is known
over the surface of an element, then interpolation will give an

accurate value at any internal point.

Within each element the potential ϕ is regarded as varying
smoothly. The variation of potential in an element with no intermediate nodes would be treated as linear with distance. If mid-side
nodes are present then a quadratic variation can be assumed as
shown in figure 3.6.

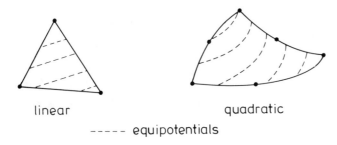

linear   quadratic

----- equipotentials

Figure 3.6   Linear and quadratic potential variation

The more intermediate nodes that are present then the better the
shape of the potential variation can be represented within an
element. However, elements with linear or quadratic variation are
most commonly used. Higher order elements (cubic or quartic)
may not necessarily give better results, especially if the actual
potential variation is linear or quadratic, as the extra terms may
produce spurious values of the derivatives.

As a first step to solution the computer program will assemble a
matrix of simultaneous equations relating the potential at each node
to that at each of the other nodes in the elements which touch it.
The matrix which results is sparse and symmetric about the leading
diagonal (see chapter 4).

These equations can be obtained by several different approaches.
The easiest of these to understand is the method of minimum energy.
(Perhaps more common is the Galerkin weighted residual method
Finlayson, 1972)).

The stored energy ΔW within a small volume ΔV of the system due to the electrostatic field and any charges present is given by:

$$\delta W = (\tfrac{1}{2} \epsilon_o \epsilon_r \bar{E}^2 + \tfrac{1}{2} \rho\phi)\delta V \qquad (3.13)$$

The total energy within the volume of an element is therefore:

$$W_e = \int_e \tfrac{1}{2}(\epsilon_o \epsilon_r \bar{E}^2 + \rho\phi)dV + \int_s \frac{\sigma\phi}{2} dS \qquad (3.14)$$

where σ is the surface charge and the integral S is over the surface of the element. This surface charge term must for each area of charge be attributed to one element only.

Now, if there are n nodes within an element and their potentials are ϕ_1 to ϕ_n the potential at any point within the element can be expressed as:

$$\phi = \phi_1 N_1 + \phi_2 N_2 + \ldots\ldots + \phi_n N_n \qquad (3.15)$$

where the values N_1 to N_n are dependent only on the geometry of the element and the position in space of the point under consideration and are known as 'shape functions'. These functions are chosen such that they have a value of 1 at the node with their own number and become zero at any other node in the element. Thus it may be observed that ϕ takes the value ϕ_1 at node 1, ϕ_2 at node 2 and so on.

If in the element the same shape functions can be applied to the variation of both ϕ and the spacial coordinates then the element is said to be 'isoparametric'.

The components of E in the three directions will be given by:

$$E_x = - \sum_{i=1}^{n} \phi_i \frac{\partial N_i}{\partial x}$$

$$E_y = - \sum_{i=1}^{n} \phi_i \frac{\partial N_i}{\partial y}$$

$$E_z = - \sum_{i=1}^{n} \phi_i \frac{\partial N_i}{\partial z} \tag{3.16}$$

They can thus be expressed in terms of the gradients of the shape functions.

The expression for the stored energy within the element now becomes:

$$W_e = \int_e \left\{ \tfrac{1}{2} \varepsilon_o \varepsilon_r \left[\left(\sum_{i=1}^{n} \phi_i \frac{\partial N_i}{\partial x} \right)^2 + \left(\sum_{i=1}^{n} \phi_i \frac{\partial N_i}{\partial y} \right)^2 \right. \right.$$

$$\left. \left. + \left(\sum_{i=1}^{n} \phi_i \frac{\partial N_i}{\partial z} \right)^2 \right] + \frac{\rho}{2} \left(\sum_{i=1}^{n} \phi_i N_i \right) \right\} dV + \int_s \frac{\sigma}{2} \sum_{i=1}^{n} \phi_i N_i dS \tag{3.17}$$

For the condition of minimum energy it is required that

$$\frac{\partial W_e}{\partial \phi_i} = 0$$

for all nodal values of ϕ within an element. This means that equation (3.17) must be differentiated with respect to each of the nodal values in turn.

For our 'n' node element this gives rise to a series of n equations.

$$\int_e \left\{ \varepsilon_o \varepsilon_r \left[\frac{\partial N_j}{\partial x} (\sum_{i=1}^{n} \phi_i \frac{\partial N_i}{\partial x}) + \frac{\partial N_j}{\partial y} (\sum_{i=1}^{n} \phi_i \frac{\partial N_i}{\partial y}) + \frac{\partial N_j}{\partial z} (\sum_{i=1}^{n} \phi_i \frac{\partial N_i}{\partial z}) \right] \right.$$

$$\left. + \frac{\rho}{2} \sum_{i=1}^{n} N_i \right\} dV + \int_s \frac{1}{2} \sum_{i=1}^{n} \sigma N_i \, dS = 0 \qquad (3.18)$$

where $j = 1,n$.

This integration is usually performed over each element using a numerical method such as Gaussian Quadrature. The equations from the individual elements are then combined to produce a matrix where the known values of charge distribution constitute the right hand sides.

In order to solve the equations the boundary conditions must be set. Where the nodal potentials are prescribed, a boundary is of the Dirichlet type and terms including the relevant nodes will form part of the right hand sides of the equations. Where the normal derivative of potential is zero at a boundary, this is equivalent to setting the surface charge to zero. This is a Neumann boundary, i.e. a natural boundary which allows no flux leakage ($\frac{\partial \phi}{\partial n} = 0$).

The procedure used is to map the element on to a normalised element. For instance, a six noded triangular element with curved sides would be mapped on to a normalised triangle of unit area as shown in figure 3.7.

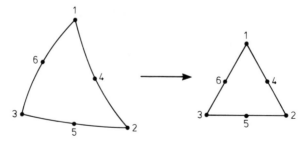

Figure 3.7   Mapping on to a normalised quadratic element

Area coordinates are used on the normalised triangle. These can be found for any point within the triangle by drawing lines to any two vertices and computing the area enclosed by these two lines and the side joining the vertices. Thus, the coordinates of the vertices themselves will be given by: (1,0,0), (0,1,0) and (0,0,1), and the coordinates of the mid side nodes will be: (0.5, 0.5, 0), (0, 0.5, 0.5) and (0.5, 0, 0.5). Appendix 2 gives tables of normalised coordinates (L1, L2, L3) for numerical integration over triangles. Values of the function F to be integrated (see equation (3.18)) must be evaluated at each of the m integrating points. The integral is then given by the summation:

$$I \;=\; \sum_{i=1}^{m} W_i \; F(L_1, L_2, L_3) \qquad\qquad (3.19)$$

where W_i are the weights (which are also tabulated).

Curvilinear rectangular elements are mapped on to a normalised rectangle where the coordinate limits are −1 to +1 in each direction as shown in figure 3.8.

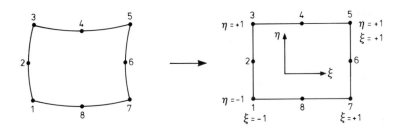

Figure 3.8   Mapping on to a normalised rectangular element

Tables of normalised coordinates for numerical integration are also given in Appendix 2 and the summation to obtain the integral is performed similarly to that for triangular elements. Zienkiewiez (1977) gives more extensive tables.

With 3 dimensional elements the most commonly used element is 20 node 'brick'. The 15 node wedge element is used as a 'filler' in places where the 'brick' will not fit the topology. The 'brick' element is mapped on to a normalised cube which has coordinates going from −1 to +1 in each of the three directions. The wedge element is mapped on to a normalised wedge which uses area coordinates for planes parallel to the triangular faces and cartesian coordinates from −1 to +1 in the direction transverse to this.

Numerical integration in three dimensions is performed as follows. The 'brick' element is transformed to a normalised cube and the integration formula is used as for the rectangle but in all three directions. For the prism element the integration formulae for the triangle may be applied in the directions of the triangular end faces. For the third dimension the formula for the rectangle must be used. Alternatively, there exist integration schemes, Hammer et al. (1956), specially designed for three dimensional elements. These are of particular use for shapes such as tetrahedra.

The shape functions for various elements which have quadratic variation are given in Appendix A.

In order to compute the values of the derivatives $\frac{\partial N_i}{\partial x}$, $\frac{\partial N_i}{\partial y}$ and $\frac{\partial N_i}{\partial z}$ required in the evaluation of the coefficients in equation (3.18) a transformation is required from the normalised coordinates to the system used in the actual problem.

Direct differentiation of the shape functions gives:

$$
\begin{bmatrix} \dfrac{\partial N_i}{\partial \xi} \\[2ex] \dfrac{\partial N_i}{\partial \eta} \\[2ex] \dfrac{\partial N_i}{\partial \zeta} \end{bmatrix}
=
\begin{bmatrix} \dfrac{\partial x}{\partial \xi} & \dfrac{\partial y}{\partial \xi} & \dfrac{\partial z}{\partial \xi} \\[2ex] \dfrac{\partial x}{\partial \eta} & \dfrac{\partial y}{\partial \eta} & \dfrac{\partial z}{\partial \eta} \\[2ex] \dfrac{\partial x}{\partial \zeta} & \dfrac{\partial y}{\partial \zeta} & \dfrac{\partial z}{\partial \zeta} \end{bmatrix}
\begin{bmatrix} \dfrac{\partial N_i}{\partial x} \\[2ex] \dfrac{\partial N_i}{\partial y} \\[2ex] \dfrac{\partial N_i}{\partial z} \end{bmatrix}
=
[J]
\begin{bmatrix} \dfrac{\partial N_i}{\partial x} \\[2ex] \dfrac{\partial N_i}{\partial y} \\[2ex] \dfrac{\partial N_i}{\partial z} \end{bmatrix}
\qquad (3.20)
$$

where [J] is known as the Jacobian matrix.

The inverse of [J] is required in order to express the spacial derivatives in local coordinates

$$
\begin{bmatrix}
\dfrac{\partial N_i}{\partial x} \\[2ex]
\dfrac{\partial N_i}{\partial y} \\[2ex]
\dfrac{\partial N_i}{\partial z}
\end{bmatrix}
= [J]^{-1}
\begin{bmatrix}
\dfrac{\partial N_i}{\partial \xi} \\[2ex]
\dfrac{\partial N_i}{\partial \eta} \\[2ex]
\dfrac{\partial N_i}{\partial \zeta}
\end{bmatrix}
\tag{3.21}
$$

Also, in order to perform the integrations over the real volume in terms of the normalised coordinates, it is necessary to use the relationship;

$$dV = dx.dy.dz = DET[J]d\xi.d\eta.d\zeta$$

where DET[J] is the determinant of the Jacobian matrix.

Equations 3.18 now become:

$$
\int_e \left\{ \epsilon_o \epsilon_r \left[\frac{\partial N_j}{\partial x} \sum_{i=1}^{n} \left(\phi_i \frac{\partial N_i}{\partial x} \right) + \frac{\partial N_j}{\partial y} \sum_{i=1}^{n} \left(\phi_i \frac{\partial N_i}{\partial y} \right) + \frac{\partial N_j}{\partial z} \sum_{i=1}^{n} \left(\phi_i \frac{\partial N_i}{\partial z} \right) \right. \right.
$$

$$
\left. \left. + \frac{\rho}{2} \sum_{i=1}^{n} N_i \right] DET[J] \; . \; d\xi.d\eta.d\zeta \right.
\tag{3.22}
$$

For an isoparametric element the individual elements of the Jacobian can be evaluated by substituting x, y and z in turn for ϕ in equation (3.15) and differentiating with respect to the normalised variable. The integral for the surface charges may also be evaluated in a similar way using the Jacobian for the relevant surface facets. In a two dimensional system with cartesian coordinates the above equations may be replaced by a reduced set with only terms corresponding to the two directions. This means that the matrices will now be 2 x 2. In axisymmetric problems the total volume δV of an element is $\int 2\pi r \, dS$ where r is the radius at any point on the element and S

32

is the surface of cross section of the element. Equation (3.14) will
now take the form:

$$W_e = 2\pi \int_s \frac{r}{2} (\varepsilon_o \varepsilon_r \bar{E}^2 + \rho\phi)dS + 2\ell \int_\ell \frac{r\sigma\phi d\ell}{2}$$

where ℓ is a line of surface containing any applied charges.

For many cases it may be sufficient to replace the factor r in the
first term of the integral by the value of radius at the centroid of
an element and the factor r in the second term by the average radius
of the area over which the charges are prescribed. Errors may
however occur in the neighbourhood of the axis of rotation. A better
method is to fit the value of r to the shape function and integrate
exactly. A detailed treatment of this method may be found in Hinton
and Owen (1979). During the matrix assembly process it is common
practice to store the values of the derivatives of the shape functions
at the nodes of each element, for use later in the computation of
electric fields. When the matrix of equations has been solved for
the nodal potentials the user may then require values at other points
in the model. These may be calculated using the shape functions once
more and applying equation (3.15). Computation of smooth electric
fields within the model is rather less easy.

It is possible to use the shape function derivatives within an
element, applying equation (3.16) directly. However, the same
problem arises as is experienced using the Finite Difference Method.
Fields then appear to be discontinuous across element boundaries.
A scheme such as the following is recommended. Field components at
the nodes for each element are calculated using the previously
stored values of the shape function derivatives and applying equation
(3.16). Each node in the system will have a separate set of values
for each element which touches it. Values of each component at each
node are averaged to give a single set of nodal field values, except
at dielectric boundaries where there will need to be a separate set

for each material, and care must be taken that the correct continuity
conditions are maintained.

3.3 COMPUTATION OF FORCES IN ELECTROSTATICS

Where it is required to calculate the force on an object or group
of objects in an electrostatic system, if the fields can be computed
over a surface enveloping the object then the forces and torques
may be computed.

The recommended method (Silvester et al (1977) and Zienkiewicz et
al (1983)) is to integrate the electrostatic stress, which is a
tensor quantity, over the surface.

For a surface where the field vector $\bar{E}$ does not lie along the normal
it can be shown that the direction of stress $\bar{t}$ lies in the plane of $\bar{E}$
and n in a direction such that $\bar{E}$ bisects the angle between n and $\bar{t}$.

Figure 3.9 Stress due
             to an
             electric
             field on
             a surface

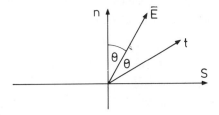

where

$$|t| = \frac{\varepsilon_o \bar{E}^2}{2}$$

If the angle θ between the outward normal and $\bar{E}$ is less than 45°
then the normal component of pressure will be such as to exert a
pull on the enclosed object(s), but if the angle θ is more than 45°
the normal component will be inwards. Integration of the components
of $\bar{t}$ over a dielectric surface may be difficult, as the shape of the
surface may be complex and the curvatures of the field lines may be
large. Therefore the recommended procedure is to draw a 'box' around
the object in space and calculate the integrated stress over its
surface. For example:

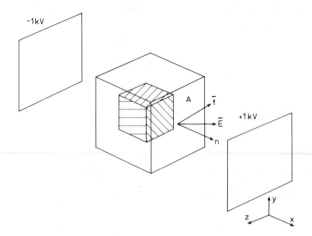

Figure 3.10   Dielectric block in electric field

In this example a dielectric block is suspended between two charged
plates. The electric field components are mapped over each surface
of the box. The three components of force are now computed for each
field point on the box and the integrals evaluated. The values are
summed for the six sides, and the net force calculated.

Thus for surface A, if θ is the angle between $\bar{E}$ and the normal to
the surface and α is the angle made by the projection of $\bar{E}$ on the
surface and the YZ plane:

$$F_x = \int_A \frac{\varepsilon_o \bar{E}^2}{2} \cos 2\theta \, . \, da,$$

$$F_y = \int_A \frac{\varepsilon_o \bar{E}^2}{2} \sin 2\theta \, . \, \cos \alpha \, . \, da$$

$$F_z = \int_A \frac{\varepsilon_o \bar{E}^2}{2} \sin 2\theta \, . \, \sin \alpha \, . \, da$$

The other surfaces will be treated similarly.

The torque τ on the object is given by:

$$\tau = \int_s \bar{r} \times (\bar{t}.n)\,da$$

where $\bar{r}$ is the distance from an arbitrary point in space.

3.4 CHOICE OF METHOD

The choice of method to be used in solving a problem in electrostatics will depend on:

a) What computer programs are available?

b) Is it a 2 dimensional or 3 dimensional problem?

c) How complicated is the geometry and can it be easily represented by simple analytical shapes?

d) What information is required and how accurate must the answers be?

e) How much manual effort is involved in assembling the data and how expensive is the computer program to run?

If a large amount of manual effort is involved in assembling and checking the input data to a program then this can in many cases far outweigh the cost of the final computation. Thus it is probably economically most advantageous to use a package which has good interactive data input and good error checking facilities.

Modern computer packages may be regarded as having three separate functions:

1) A pre-processor which enables the user to build up his data in a conversational mode. The output from this part of the program may be written up at any time to a database where it is stored for future modification or for access by the solution program.

2) A solver which takes the data and produces a potential solution. The solution potentials along with the

input data are then written once more to the database.

3) A post-processor which reads the data and solution
   potentials from the database and allows the user to
   plot fields, potentials or perhaps other parameters
   over any desired region or line.

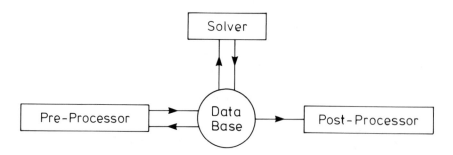

Figure 3.11   Data transfer in a finite element program

The use of graphical output is a great time saver when a user
requires to know whether his or her data is meaningful. If a
Finite Element program is available for solving a 2 or 3 dimensional
problem then it should be possible to get an acceptable solution
provided that there is sufficient core in the computer to enable a
fine enough mesh to be used. However, other methods may be cheaper
to run. In order to provide some guidance to the user a table of
advantages and disadvantages is provided overleaf:

Method	Advantage(s)	Disadvantage(s)
Analytic (Including conformal transformation)	Very fast. No need to specify outer boundary.	Only deals with simple shapes.
Integral[†] (Including image charges and surface integrals)	Fast solution for charges and surface fields. No need to specify outer boundary.	Computation of fields from solution is slower than for differential methods for the same number of mesh points. A full matrix is produced for the solution phase requiring more core than for differential F.E. method with same mesh size.
Finite difference	Moderately fast solution with good economy of computer core. Fields are cheap to compute from potential solution.	Difficult to represent complex geometries unless a fine mesh is specified. Outer boundary must be specified.
Finite Element	Mesh can be designed to fit complex geometries. Sparse matrix permits fast solution with economy of core. Fields are cheap to compute from potentials.	With existing programs outer boundary must be specified.
Monte Carlo [‡]	Fast potential solution.	Field evaluation is slow.

[†] [‡] not considered in present text but a brief description of both the Monte Carlo and Boundary Integral methods is given in appendix D.

Whichever method is used, where it is necessary to discretise the model, care should be taken in the neighbourhood of small radii on electrode surfaces. Sharp points can never be properly represented because the fields theoretically approach infinity here. Potential values may be computed correctly but accuracy of fields will depend on the fineness of the mesh around a curved electrode.

If the Finite Element method is chosen then it is necessary to ensure that the shape of the elements is acceptable. With triangular elements the aim should be to make them as close as possible to equilateral, although a ratio of 2 to 1 in lengths of sides could be tolerated. Similarly, with quadrilateral elements, the best results are obtained if the corner angles approximate to right angles, and the ratio of sides should again be within a factor of 2 to 1.

One of the limitations of differential methods is the need to specify an outer boundary to the problem. For cases where a closed region is under investigation this does not matter, but when the real boundary is at infinity then the usual procedure has been to place an artificial earthed boundary sufficiently far out that the errors induced are acceptable. This however is expensive in that there may be a considerable number of mesh elements in which the user has no interest in the solution. Two techniques have been used to overcome this. These are:

(a) Ballooning, (Silvester et al (1977));

(b) Infinite elements, (Zienkiewicz et al (1983)).

These are described in the literature and it is expected that packages will in future incorporate one of these methods.

REFERENCES

Allen, D.N. de G. (1954). Relaxation Methods, McGraw Hill, New York.

Carre, B.A. (1961). The determination of the optimum accelerating factor for successive over-relaxation. Computer J., 4, p. 73.

Finlayson, B.A. (1972). The method of weighted residuals and variational principles. Academic Press, New York.

Forsythe, G.E. and Wasow, W.R. (1960). Finite difference methods for partial differential equations. John Wiley and Sons, New York.

Hammer, P.C., Marlowe, O.P. and Stroud, A.H. (1956). Numerical integration over simplexes and cones, Math. Tables Aids Comp., 10, 130-137.

Hinton, E., Owen, D.R.J. (1979). An introduction to finite element computations, Pineridge Press, Swansea, U.K.

Silvester, P.P., Lowther, D.A., Carpenter, C.J., Wyatt, E.A. (1977). Exterior finite elements for 2-dimensional field problems with open boundaries, Proc. IEE, 124, 1267-1270.

Southwell, R.V. (1946). Relaxation methods in theoretical physics, Oxford University Press.

Zienkiewicz, O.C. (1977). The finite element method, 3rd Edition, McGraw Hill, New York.

Zienkiewicz, O.C., Emson, C., Betess, P. (1983). A novel boundary infinite element, IJNME, 19, 393-404.

CHAPTER 4
Equation Solving

INTRODUCTION

The heaviest use of computer time and core storage in any finite
element analysis, (with the possible exception of mesh generation),
is encountered in the equation solving stage. The basic matrix
equation which has been generated by the finite element analysis is
of the form:

$$Ax = b \qquad\qquad (4.1)$$

where A is a sparse, symmetrical n x n matrix, x and b are column
vectors of dimension n, n being the number of nodes in the problem.

A wide variety of methods (Jacobs, (1981)) is available for the
solution of such matrices. The range of methods fall into two broad
categories - Direct and Indirect methods. Direct methods obtain the
required solution to the matrix equation without recourse to intermediate approximation. Indirect methods, on the other hand, start
from an initial approximation and proceed by calculating a sequence
of further approximations which, hopefully, converges to the required
solution.

Direct methods generally have the disadvantage of requiring more
computation and greater quantities of core storage. On the other
hand, direct methods have the advantage of being less complex, easier
to program and somewhat more robust.

Indirect methods, requiring less calculation, tend to be faster for large problems. Their very nature, however, can lead to problems when dealing with ill-conditioned matrices. The increased complexity of indirect methods can also be prohibitive to the less experienced programmer.

In this chapter a brief introduction to the main features of the matrix equation which is to be solved, is given. Several possible solution methods are outlined and the reader is directed to further literature, covering solution methods in greater depth. No attempt has been made to give a complete review. Where possible, published source coding for matrix solution is referenced, allowing tested solvers to be obtained, without the necessity to resort to extensive programming.

4.1 FEATURES OF THE A MATRIX

The general matrix equation to be solved for a linear electrostatic problem is given by equation 4.1.

The A matrix is symmetrical about the leading diagonal and sparse. The non-zero entries in A form a definite pattern. This pattern is determined by the arrangement of nodes which define the problem to be solved, or more precisely, how the nodes are interconnected.

For example, the nine noded eight triangle mesh shown below (figure 4.1), would generate an A matrix with non-zeros as indicated.

$$
\begin{array}{c c}
& \begin{array}{c c c c c c c c c}
1 & 2 & 3 & 4 & 5 & 6 & 7 & 8 & 9
\end{array} \\
\begin{array}{c}
1 \\ 2 \\ 3 \\ 4 \\ 5 \\ 6 \\ 7 \\ 8 \\ 9
\end{array} &
\left[
\begin{array}{c c c c c c c c c}
x & x & & & & & & x & x \\
x & x & x & x & & & & & x \\
& x & x & x & & & & & \\
& x & x & x & x & & & & x \\
& & & x & x & x & & & x \\
& & & & x & x & x & x & x \\
& & & & & x & x & x & \\
x & & & & & & x & x & x & x \\
x & x & & & x & x & x & & x & x
\end{array}
\right]
\end{array}
$$

Figure 4.1

42

Non-zero entries occur on each of the diagonal locations plus
locations (i,j) and (j,i), where i and j are nodes common to any
triangle.

For direct solution methods in particular, it is advantageous, from
the point of view of efficient matrix storage, to group the non-zero
elements as close as possible to the leading diagonal. This may be
achieved by renumbering the nodes so as to achieve the smallest
possible difference between node numbers common to any one element.
Such an arrangement, for the example given in figure 4.1, (which is
not necessarily unique) is shown below (figure 4.2).

$$
\begin{array}{c}
 \\
1 \\
2 \\
3 \\
4 \\
5 \\
6 \\
7 \\
8 \\
9
\end{array}
\begin{array}{ccccccccc}
1 & 2 & 3 & 4 & 5 & 6 & 7 & 8 & 9 \\
x & x &   & x & x &   &   &   &   \\
x & x & x &   & x & x &   &   &   \\
  & x & x &   &   & x &   &   &   \\
x &   &   & x & x &   & x & x &   \\
x & x &   & x & x & x &   & x & x \\
  & x & x &   & x & x &   &   & x \\
  &   &   & x &   &   & x & x &   \\
  &   &   & x & x &   & x & x & x \\
  &   &   &   & x & x &   & x & x
\end{array}
$$

Figure 4.2

In this case, all the non-zero entries fall within 5 rows or columns
of the leading diagonal. The matrix is thus said to be banded, with
a half-bandwidth of 5.

Such renumbering may be achieved either by careful selection of node
ordering or by employing a renumbering algorithm. (A selection of
renumbering algorithms is presented in the references). The great
advantage of reorganising the matrix into a banded form, is in the
core storage savings which may be achieved. As has been stated, the
A matrix is symmetrical about the leading diagonal; consequently, to
fully define the matrix, only the elements within the upper (or lower)
half band need be stored. In the above example, a 9 x 5 rectangular

matrix contains sufficient information to specify the full A matrix.

```
       1  2  3  4  5                          1  2  3  4  5  6  7  8  9
    1 ┌ x  x     x  x ┐                    1 ┌ x  x     x  x             ┐
    2 │ x  x     x  x │                    2 │    x  x     x  x          │
    3 │ x        x    │                    3 │       x        x          │
    4 │ x  x     x  x │                    4 │          x  x     x  x    │
    5 │ x  x     x  x │   Equivalent       5 │             x  x     x  x │
    6 │ x        x    │       to           6 │                x        x │
    7 │ x  x          │                    7 │  symmetrical      x  x    │
    8 │ x  x          │                    8 │                      x  x │
    9 └ x             ┘                    9 └                         x ┘
```

Figure 4.3

In this example, the storage requirement for the A matrix has been reduced from 9 x 9 = 81 to 9 x 5 = 45, a 44% saving. As the problem size increases, the relative saving also increases. Take, for example, a modestly sized finite element program of 500 nodes. The complete A matrix has 500 x 500 = 250,000 entries, sufficient to swamp the core storage of most medium to large computers. Such a problem might typically have a half bandwidth of 25. By storing only the upper half bandwidth in a rectangular matrix the storage requirement drops to 12,500 entries, bringing the problem down to mini-computer size.

Even greater savings may be obtained by recognising that a large percentage of the entries within the bandwidth are zero. By storing only the non-zero entries along with pointers to their location, the A matrix storage requirement may be further reduced. This technique is, however, only suitable for certain indirect methods. In general the non-zeros within the bandwidth tend to be filled-in using direct solution methods.

4.2   DIRECT METHODS

4.2.1 Gaussian Elimination

Gaussian elimination is the simplest of the methods available for the solution of our matrix equation. It is based on the observations that an upper (or lower) triangular system of n equations as shown below, may be readily solved:

$$
\begin{bmatrix}
a_{11} & a_{12} & \cdot & \cdot & \cdot & \cdot & \cdot & a_{1n} \\
 & a_{22} & \cdot & & & & & a_{2n} \\
 & & \cdot & & & & & \cdot \\
 & & & \cdot & & & & \cdot \\
 & & & & & & & \cdot \\
 & & & & a_{n-1\ n-1} & & a_{n-1.n} \\
 & & & & & & & a_{nn}
\end{bmatrix}
\begin{bmatrix}
x_1 \\ x_2 \\ \cdot \\ \cdot \\ \cdot \\ x_{n-1} \\ x_n
\end{bmatrix}
=
\begin{bmatrix}
b_1 \\ b_2 \\ \cdot \\ \cdot \\ \cdot \\ b_{n-1} \\ b_n
\end{bmatrix}
$$

$$(4.2)$$

The solution is obtained by back substitution. (Using the nth equation to eliminate x_n from each of the remaining equations one may then progress to eliminate x_{n-1} etc. in a similar manner).

Consequently, if a general n x n A matrix can be transformed into upper triangular form, this approach provides a simple solution method. The easiest way in which this transformation may be achieved is by using the ith equation to eliminate the terms i + 1 to n in the ith column. This process is illustrated using the 3 x 3 matrix illustrated overleaf.

The advantages of this method lie in its inherent simplicity and robustness. The number of numerical operations is, however, large and despite utilising efficient storage methods, the storage requirement can still be substantial.

(i) $\begin{bmatrix} 1 & 2 & 3 \\ 3 & 2 & 1 \\ 2 & 1 & 3 \end{bmatrix} \begin{bmatrix} x_1 \\ x_2 \\ x_3 \end{bmatrix} = \begin{bmatrix} 14 \\ 10 \\ 13 \end{bmatrix}$ (iv) $x_3 = 9/3 = 3$

(ii) $\begin{bmatrix} 1 & 2 & 3 \\ 0 & -4 & -8 \\ 0 & -3 & -3 \end{bmatrix} \begin{bmatrix} x_1 \\ x_2 \\ x_3 \end{bmatrix} = \begin{bmatrix} 14 \\ -32 \\ -15 \end{bmatrix}$ (v) $x_2 = (-32 + 3 \times 8)/-4 = 2$

(iii) $\begin{bmatrix} 1 & 2 & 3 \\ 0 & -4 & -8 \\ 0 & 0 & 3 \end{bmatrix} \begin{bmatrix} x_1 \\ x_2 \\ x_3 \end{bmatrix} = \begin{bmatrix} 14 \\ -32 \\ 9 \end{bmatrix}$ (vi) $x_1 = (14 - 2 \times 2 - 3 \times 3)$
$= 1$

           Triangulation   Back Substitution

Improvements in the accuracy of solution, using this method, may be made using such techniques as partial pivoting. This approach is, in general, not suitable for the solution of banded systems of equations, as the bandwidth can be radically increased by the pivotal step. In general, for the type of A matrix encountered in electrostatic problems, the diagonal terms are non-zero and dominant, giving little advantage to these more complex algorithms.

4.2.2 LU Decomposition

LU decomposition depends on the fact that, under certain conditions, a matrix S may be expressed as

$$S = LU \tag{4.3}$$

where L is a unit lower triangular matrix of the form

$$\begin{bmatrix} 1 & & & & \\ L_{21} & 1 & & 0 & \\ \cdot & \cdot & & & \\ \cdot & & \cdot & & \\ L_{n1} & \cdots & & L_{n.n-1} & 1 \end{bmatrix}$$

and U is an upper triangular matrix of the form

$$
\begin{bmatrix}
U_{11} & U_{12} & \cdot & & \cdot & U_{1n} \\
 & U_{22} & & & & \\
 & & \cdot & & & \cdot \\
 & & & \cdot & & \cdot \\
 & & & & \cdot & U_{n-1.n} \\
 & & & & & U_{nn}
\end{bmatrix}
$$

Assuming the matrix A satisfies these conditions, the equation Ax = B
may be rewritten in the form

$\qquad$ LUx = b $\hspace{6cm}$ (4.4)

which may in turn be separated in to two equations

$\qquad$ y = Ux $\qquad$ and $\qquad$ Ly = b $\hspace{4cm}$ (4.5)

As we have already seen in section 4.2.1, an upper or lower triangular
system may be readily solved using back substitution. Thus by
solving for y and then substituting, we may obtain the solution for x.

The decomposition of A into lower and upper triangular form is a
comparatively mechanical process an algorithm for which may be
found in Bell (1975). This method is amenable to being handled in a
banded form in a similar manner to Gaussian Elimination.

4.3   INDIRECT METHODS

4.3.1 Bifactorisation

This method is similar to LU decomposition (see section 4.2.2) in
that the ultimate aim is to solve the matrix equation by substituting
an alternative expression for A. In this case the equation

$\qquad$ $L^{(n)} \cdot L^{(n-1)} \ldots L^{(1)} \cdot A \cdot R^{(1)} \ldots R^{(n-1)} \cdot R^{(n)} = I$ $\hspace{1.5cm}$ (4.6)

is modified to yield

$$A^{-1} = R^{(1)} . R^{(2)} ... R^{(n)} . L^{(n)} ... L^{(2)} . L^{(1)} \qquad (4.7)$$

Thus allowing us to solve the matrix equation, rewritten in the form

$$x = A^{-1} b \qquad (4.8)$$

The $R^{(j)}$ and $L^{(j)}$ matrices may be obtained from the following sequence of operations:

$$A^{(0)} = A$$
$$A^{(1)} = L^{(1)} A^{(0)} R^{(1)}$$
$$A^{(2)} = L^{(2)} A^{(1)} R^{(2)}$$

.

.

.

$$A^{(n)} = L^{(n)} A^{(n-1)} R^{(n)} = 1$$

In general, $A^{(j)}$, $L^{(j)}$, and $R^{(j)}$, may be computed from $A^{(j-1)}$. i.e.

$A^{(j)}$

$$a_{jj}^{(j)} = 1; \qquad a_{ij}^{(j)} = 0; \qquad a_{jk}^{(j)} = 0$$

$$a_{ik}^{(j)} = a_{ik}^{(j-1)} - \frac{a_{ij}^{(j-1)} . a_{jk}^{(j-1)}}{a_{jj}^{(j-1)}} \qquad (4.9)$$

where i and k = (j+1), ... n.

$L^{(j)}$

Differs from unity matrix only in column (j)

i.e.

$$L^{(j)} = \begin{bmatrix} 1 & & 0 & & \\ & 1 & 0 & & \\ & & L_{ij} & & \\ & & \vdots & 1 & \\ & & L_{nj} & & 1 \end{bmatrix} \qquad (4.10)$$

$$L_{jj}{}^{(j)} = \frac{1}{a_{jj}{}^{(j-1)}}$$

$$L_{ij}{}^{(j)} = -a_{ij}{}^{(j-1)}/a_{jj}{}^{(j-1)} \qquad k = (j+1) \dots n$$

$\underline{R^{(j)}}$

Differs from unity matrix only in row (j).

i.e.

$$R^{(j)} = \begin{bmatrix} 1 & & & & & \\ & 1 & & & & \\ 0 & 0 & 1 & r_{ij+1}{}^{(i)} & \dots & r_{jn}{}^{(i)} \\ & & & 1 & & \\ & & & & & 1 \end{bmatrix} \qquad (4.11)$$

$$r_{jk}{}^{(j)} = -1_{jk}{}^{(j-1)}/a_{jj}{}^{(j-1)} \qquad k = (j+1) \dots n$$

4.3.2 Conjugate Gradient

The conjugate gradient method belongs to the same family of techniques as the method of steepest descent. The method requires an initial approximation to the solution x_o, from which it seeks to obtain the minimum of an appropriate measure of the residual from the equation

$$r = b - Ax \qquad (4.12)$$

(When a series of repeated solutions of a problem is required, using the same geometry with different material properties or conditions, savings in computation may be obtained by using the solution obtained for one problem as the initial approximation for the next.)

Minimisation of the residual is obtained by computing a series of estimates x_i for which the residual is r_i. Each estimate is obtained by regarding the solution for n unknowns as a point in an η dimensional space. Each direction of search is as near as possible to the line of steepest descent but normal to all previous directions. When $r_i = \bar{0}$, the exact solution is obtained.

One such algorithm is illustrated below:

For a given starting vector x_o. The residual may be calculated

$$r_o = b - Ax_o$$

Set the first search direction vector

$$r_i = r_o$$

Then for $i = 0, 1, \ldots, n-1$, calculate the coefficient

$$\alpha_i = \frac{p_i^T r_i}{p_i^T A p_i}$$

Set the new estimate

$$x_{i+1} = x_i + \alpha_i p_i$$

Evaluate the residual

$$r_{i+1} = b - Ax_{i+1}$$

Calculate the coeffficient

$$\beta_i = - \frac{r_{i+1}^T A p_i}{p_i^T A p_i}$$

Determine the new search direction

$$p_{i+1} = r_{i+1} + \beta_i p_i$$

The method, given exact calculation, will give the exact solution in n steps. However, due to numerical error and limitations in computer precision, the method behaves as an iterative technique. Its great advantage lies in that, after only a few iterations, the residual is generally sufficiently small to allow the x vector to be taken as a solution.

Further benefits may be derived from adopting more sophisticated techniques such as ICCG (Incomplete Cholesky Factorisation with Conjugate Gradients) or alternative methods of pre-conditioning, some of which are referred to in the bibliography. These enable a good approximate solution to be obtained in much less than n steps.

(Bandwidth reduction is not necessary with conjugate gradient methods.)

4.4   BANDWIDTH REDUCTION

As was illustrated in section 4.1 bandwidth minimisation is of paramount importance in the efficient solution of finite element problems, especially when direct solution methods are employed. For simple geometries, it is often possible to arrange the node numbering so as to obtain a minimum bandwidth by inspection. For more complex meshes (and in the case of automatic mesh generation) this is not always so easy or indeed possible.

Several authors (Grooms (1972), Gibbs et al (1976), Colins (1973), and Cuthill and McKee (1969)), have produced algorithms for bandwidth reduction. Space does not permit a lengthy discussion of their relative merits or concept. In most cases, the references listed provide not only a description of the method, but also source coding for the bandwidth reduction algorithm. This should allow the reader to utilise such methods with a reasonable degree of ease.

A further efficient method of storing sparse symmetric matrices,

which is worthy of mention for completeness, is the profile method.
In this approach, only the entries below the first non-zero, and
above and including the diagonal in each column are stored. This
method is comparable to banded storage and can offer savings in
storage for certain problems. Profile reduction algorithms are also
available (Gibbs, Poole, Stockmeyer (1976)).

REFERENCES

General

Bell, W.W. (1975). Matrices for Scientists and Engineers. Van
   Nostrand Reinhold.

Curtis, A.R., Reid, J.K. (1971). Fortran Subroutines for the
   solution of sparse sets of linear equations. AERE Report No. 6844.

Jacobs, D.A.H. (1981). The solution of large system of algebraic
   equations, seminar on the numerical computation of electric and
   magnetic fields, Milan 17-19 June.

Segerlind, L.J. (1976). Applied Finite Element Analysis. Wiley.

Sherman, A.H. (1978). Algorithm 553, NSPIV - A fortran subroutine
   for sparse Gaussian elimination with partial pivoting [F4], ACM
   Transactions on Mathematical Software, 4, (4), Dec.

Indirect Methods

Biddlecombe, C. (1980). ICCBCG - A symmetric complex sparse matrix
   solver, SRC Rutherford Laboratories, CAG/80-14.

Zollenkopf, K. (1971). Bifactorisation - basic computational
   algorithm and programming techniques. Large Sparse sets of
   Linear Equations. Academic Press.

Bandwidth Reduction

Colins, R.J. (1973). Bandwidth reduction by automatic renumbering.
   International Journal of Numerical Methods in Engineering, 6,
   345-356.

Cuthill, E., McKee, J. (1969). Reducing the bandwidth of sparse
   matrices, ACM National Conference San Francisco, 157-172.

Gibbs, N.E., Poole, W.G., Stockmeyer, P.K. (1976). An algorithm for reducing the bandwidth and profile of a sparse matrix. SIAM Journal of Numerical Analysis, 13, (2), April.

Grooms, H.R. (1972). Algorithm for matrix bandwidth reduction, ASCE Journal of Structural Division, 98, ST1, 203-214.

CHAPTER 5
Practical Applications

INTRODUCTION

In recent years, electrostatics has found many useful applications
in industry. This fact, as much as any other, has provided an
added stimulus to obtaining a better understanding of electrostatic
effects. Numerical methods provide a means by which such understanding may be enhanced.

From the onset, it should be clearly stated that numerical
methods may be used to find solutions to well defined mathematical
problems. That is to say, the physical effects and the boundary
conditions of the problem may be expressed mathematically.
Numerical methods cannot be used directly to derive either of these
conditions. What the approach of numerical analysis can achieve is
the testing of ideas or concepts. If the numerical results obtained
from a 'test' formulation give plausible conclusions, then this
model may be used to derive more complex models.

It is in this interactive mode in which numerical methods are most
useful. Using experimental results at every stage to develop more
intricate models, and using these models to improve the focus of
experimental attention, one may rapidly converge to a solution to
a particular problem. Numerical methods must be thought of in the
same way as any other design tool or experimental technique. They
perform a function which is limited by their design. Inputs are
given and outputs received. One must be confident that inputs are

meaningful and that outputs are properly interpreted. A careful watch must always be maintained to ensure that results are always viewed with reference to simplifications or approximations which have been made.

With these warnings in mind, one can see that numerical methods may aid the designer in several ways:

(1) Giving an appropriate overview of the process which is modelled. This can be very useful at the early 'front end' design stage, often allowing basic misconceptions to be discarded and the primary area of interest or concern to be isolated.

(2) As the design process develops, ideas may be readily tested without necessarily designing and building expensive test equipment or experiments.

(3) A good estimate of critical dimensions such as spark gaps, maximum electrodes potential before breakdown, insulating strength or thickness, critical space charge density for incendive discharge etc. may be gained.

(4) Critical areas which have been overlooked in the design process may spring to light as a result of modelling.

(5) Perhaps one of the most valuable features of numerical modelling is the fact that one is compelled to consider in depth precisely what is going on in the process being modelled. Often the process of generating a numerical model is as valuable as the results which are obtained from it.

Once a clear understanding of the physical process which is of
interest has been obtained, you are in a position to formulate a
mathematical model for solution. In electrostatic problems this
usually involves the solution of Poisson's equation in some form:

$$\nabla^2 \phi = - \frac{\rho}{\varepsilon_o \varepsilon_r} \qquad\qquad (5.1)$$

with boundary conditions of the form:

$$\frac{\partial \phi}{\partial n} = g(s); \qquad\qquad \phi(s) = f(s) \qquad\qquad (5.2)$$

One must first ask the question - Do I have sufficient information
to specify the charge density (bulk and surface) and the dielectric
constant?

If the answer is no, one may still proceed by making an approximation; this however constitutes the first and not necessarily
trivial approximation.

If the problem which is to be modelled has symmetry, rotational
or planar, the modelling process is much simpler. Three dimensional
models devoid of such symmetry may be solved. The effort necessary
is however considerable. In many cases, an approximation to the
three dimensional problem with a geometry which has planar or
rotational symmetry, may suffice with little loss of accuracy for
certain problems. For example, it can be shown that a cubic tank,
half filled with charged liquid can be modelled quite accurately
using a rotationally symmetric cylindrical tank (see figure 5.1).
Given that the geometry of the problem can be readily specified and
that the material properties and charge distributions are available,
it is possible to derive a model for an electrostatic problem which
can be solved using numerical methods.

Why resort to numerical solutions? Can these equations be solved
analytically?

For very simple problems, analytical solutions may quite readily
be obtained. For example, the potential variation in a cylindrical
earthed metal tank, half filled with charged liquid, represents one

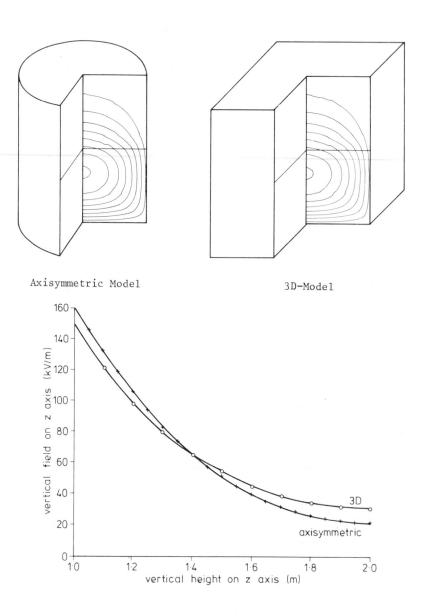

Axisymmetric Model   3D-Model

Figure 5.1   Axisymmetric approximation to a three-
dimensional problem

of the more complex arrangements for which an analytical solution may be found. If any internal protrusion or irregularity exists in such a tank it is most unlikely that an analytical solution may be obtained. Although the initial effort in establishing a model for the simple case might exceed that required for the analytical approach, extension to the more complex problem is much easier using numerical methods.

5.1 PRACTICAL CONSIDERATIONS

The term electrostatics is in many ways midleading in that although problems involve electrical effects they are generally not static. Few materials have sufficiently high resistivity to be considered perfect insulators and consequently most materials allow charge to leak to earth or relax at a rate which is not insignificant. As a result, any charge distribution which is specified for a material of finite resistivity must be seen as a time dependent function. A charged plastic sheet will discharge at a rate dependent on its surface and bulk resistivities. An earthed tank totally full of charged fuel will tend to discharge at a rate dependent on the fuel bulk conductivity. An earthed metal tank partially filled with charged fuel will discharge at a rate determined by the fuel bulk conductivity, surface conductivity, and dielectric constant. These effects may be modelled using time incremental methods if the values for bulk and surface resistivities are known. This may be done by starting at the point where charge distribution is known or assumed. A solution for the known charge distribution is obtained. Charge is then redistributed according to the field pattern which has been generated by the initial charge distribution and a new field pattern evolved. The redistribution of charge is based on the quantity of charge at a given point being moved in the direction of the field at that point, a distance determined by the fuel conductivity and time increment.

This leads on to another potential source of difficulty. Bulk and surface conductivities are normally measured in low voltage cells.

There is some evidence to suggest that measurements made in this way have no meaning when applied in a high voltage environment, a factor which is rarely borne in mind. This problem is further confounded by the apparent lack of awareness of the effect of temperature and humidity on conductivity values.

Further problems in electrostatic field modelling can exist in the interference from external effects. In many cases, electrostatic effects may be important but not dominant. For example, in filling a tank with charged liquid, the rate at which charge relaxes to the tank walls can be critical in the assessment of the onset of hazardous conditions. If however, the process of tank filling creates turbulence which alters or even dominates the relaxation process, it is not immediately obvious how such a process may be modelled. Similar effects can be experienced due to gravitational forces in electrostatic spraying and precipitation. Equally, spray droplets may be dramatically affected by aerodynamic considerations.

In order to demonstrate some of the design stages and possible pitfalls when using numerical methods the following simple problem is approached using the finite element method.

5.2 COAXIAL CAPACITOR - A LAPLACIAN PROBLEM

A square section coaxial capacitor whose length is very much greater than width, is shown in figure 5.2.

The outside wall of the capacitor is at earth potential and the inner wall at 1 kV. If we assume that the end effects of the capacitor are of no interest to us, the problem geometry and material properties do not vary in the z direction. A two dimensional per-unit-length approach may therefore be adopted in the solution. Due to the three lines of symmetry, the section can be further simplified as shown in figure 5.3. The total cross section can be shown analytically to have a capacitance per unit length of approximately $10.2 \ \varepsilon_o$ F/m.

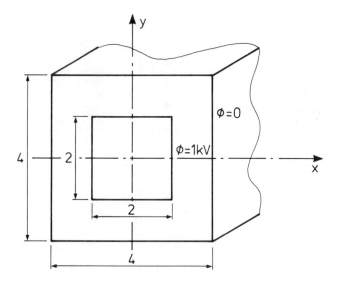

Figure 5.2   Square section coaxial capacitor

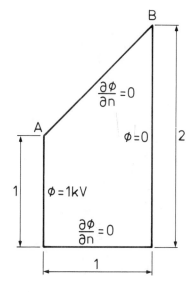

Figure 5.3   Coaxial capacitor mathematical model

60

a   9 nodes
    8 triangles

b 63 nodes
   96 triangles

c 255 nodes
  448 triangles

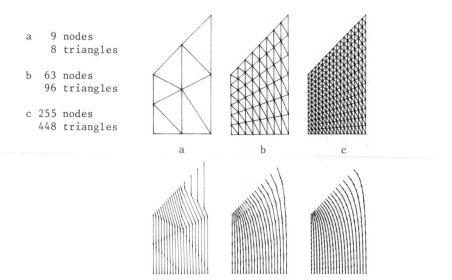

a   b   c

Figure 5.4   Coaxial capacitor - various triangular discreti-
             zations and resulting equipotential plots

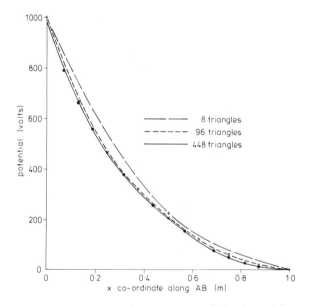

Figure 5.5   Coaxial capacitor - potential along line AB
             with increasing number of triangles

By dividing the simplified region into first order triangles and
solving for the boundary conditions shown in figure 5.3, a solution
for the potential at each of the triangle nodes and hence the total
capacitance is derived from

$$q_s = \varepsilon_o \int E \, . \, ds \qquad\qquad (5.3)$$

$$C = Q/\phi \qquad\qquad (5.4)$$

One question which is often asked is how many triangles are needed
to obtain an adequately accurate solution?

There are two answers to this question. If it is simply required
to find the total capacitance, and there is little interest in
specific values of potential or field, a surprisingly coarse mesh
is sufficient. If on the other hand a specific value of field or
potential is required, especially if it is at a point where the
potential changes rapidly (large field), then the mesh must be much
finer.

For example, three different meshes have been generated for the
particular problem illustrated above, with 8, 96, and 448 first
order triangles respectively. These meshes and the resulting
equipotential solutions are shown in figure 5.4. The values of
capacitance derived from the second of the meshes (96 triangles)
is within 6% of the analytical value and for most purposes would be
sufficiently accurate. On the other hand, the potential close to
the re-entrant corner and hence the field strength at that corner
is not accurately modelled using such a coarse mesh. This is
illustrated in figure 5.5 which shows the potential variation
across the line AB for the three meshes.

Close to the inner electrode, the potential variation is rapid
and consequently the crude discretisations used in meshes 1 and 2
are inadequate to model it accurately. Mesh 3 is, on the other hand,
sufficiently fine to give a reasonable representation of the
variation.

62

Patently, this is a simple problem which could be solved analytically. However, simply by changing two of the key dimensions,
thereby removing the symmetry of the capacitor cross section, an
analytical solution although not totally impossible becomes much
less attractive. An example of this is shown in figure 5.6. The
central electrode has been reduced in size and moved off the z axis.
In this case, there are no lines of symmetry on the cross-section
and consequently the whole area must be discretised. A possible
mesh is shown in figure 5.6 along with the resulting equipotential
plot.

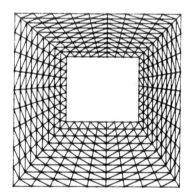 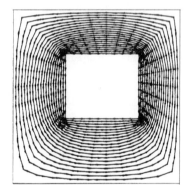

Figure 5.6   Asymmetric coaxial capacitor –
mesh and potential solution

The question of the fineness and concentration of mesh can be
further illustrated by considering the problem shown in figure 5.7.

In this problem we have a coaxial capacitor as before; however,
the central electrode has been made narrower and higher. Although
the central electrode occupies the same volume, solution of this
problem requires more careful mesh generation. Simply generating
a mesh of similar density as in the previous example would result
in the discretisation and equipotential plot shown in figure 5.8.

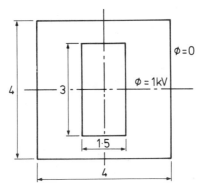

Figure 5.7   Elongated coaxial capacitor

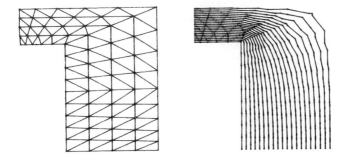

Figure 5.8   Coarse mesh

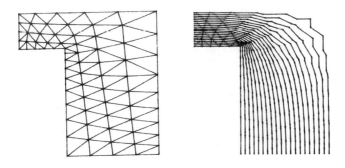

Figure 5.9   Refined mesh at re-entrant corner

The values obtained for field and potential at any re-entrant corner must be far from accurate. By modifying the mesh as shown in figure 5.9, that is concentrating the triangles around the region of rapidly changing potential, a much better solution at the re-entrant corner is achieved, at the expense of accuracy at the outside corner.

The conclusion that may be drawn from the above is that the larger the difference between the largest and the smallest significant dimension in a problem, the greater the care and the finer the discretisation which must be used.

5.3   REGIONS CONTAINING SPACE CHARGE

If an analytical solution to a problem is attempted, space charge is invariably a difficult feature to model. Use of numerical methods, however, can produce a solution with comparative ease.

Let us consider again the coaxial capacitor problem, in this case with the inter-electrode space filled with a charged cloud. This situation has been modelled and equipotential plots produced for a variety of charge densities (figures 5.10-5.13).

A space charge density of 10^{-5} C/m³ produces an electrostatic field which is heavily dominated by space charge effects. A space charge density of 10^{-8} C/m³ has negligible effect on the field distribution. Patently, these threshold values will vary according to the particular boundary conditions and geometry of the problem. However, this problem serves to illustrate one very important and useful feature of electrostatic fields. If we consider three separate conditions:

Coaxial capacitor geometry with

1)   no space charge and inner plate at 1 kV, (Figure 5.4)
2)   space charge of 5 x 10^{-8} and both plates earthed, (Figure 5.12)
3)   space charge of 5 x 10^{-8} and inner plate at 1 kV, (Figure 5.14)

65

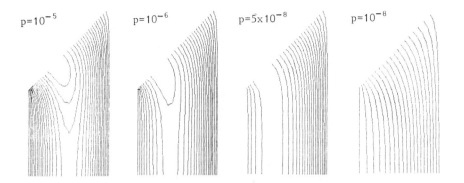

p=10⁻⁵   p=10⁻⁶   p=5x10⁻⁸   p=10⁻⁸

Figures 5.10-5.13   The effect of space charge on
potential distribution

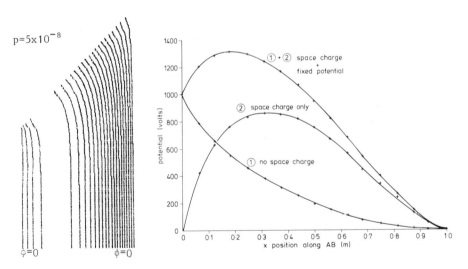

Figures 5.14-5.15   The property of superposition

The property of superposition means that, at any point in the solution region, the potential due to 1 and 2 total to equal the potential due to 3. Condition (1) is shown in figure 5.4, (3) in figure 5.12, condition (2) in figure 5.14. The effect of summing potentials along AB from conditions (1) and (2) is shown graphically in figure 5.15.

This feature can be extremely useful when deploying numerical methods. Once solutions have been obtained for the potential in a given region for a variety of boundary conditions and charge distributions, they can then be manipulated to yield potential distributions for an endless number of conditions for no extra computational effort.

5.4 COMPLEXITY OF PROBLEM

The complexity of problem which may be tackled depends on two factors:

(i)   the power of the computing facility available;

(ii) the time and effort available for obtaining a solution.

Item (ii) is the only variable which one realistically has control over. As previously stated, complex geometries require more careful discretisation. Equally, non-linear or inhomogeneous material properties require special care. The decision as to how charge distribution is modelled is often critical in obtaining an accurate problem solution and only by involved computation (described in chapter 7) can realistic inhomogeneous charge distributions be derived.

5.5 FINITE ELEMENT PACKAGES

In order to avoid the development of a special purpose program an already developed program may be used in certain cases as an alternative. The following example makes use of a well tried computer code. We are investigating in this example the electrostatic fields around an insulating bushing which is used to connect a high voltage supply into a metal tank.

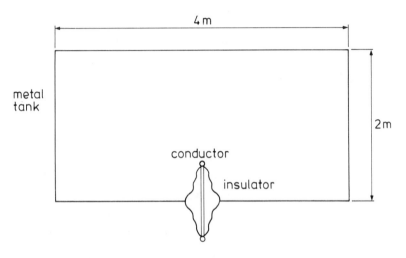

Figure 5.16   Insulating Bush in Metal Tank
The voltage on the lead-through is 100 kV.

The problem is axisymmetric and the computer program used is the
PE2D finite element package from Rutherford Appleton Laboratory
(RAL) [Biddlecombe et al, (1981)].   This is an interactive package
which houses the pre-processor and post-processor in one program
and has a separate module for the solution phase. Data input to the
pre and post processor program is in the form of a series of
commands. Each command may be followed on the same logical line
by one or more parameters. Each parameter definition is followed
by a comma or a space. A trailing comma indicates a continuation
on the next line. The example shows the commands in this form which
are required to run the program. Other modes of command input are
available although not shown here. These are:

a) Positional parameters.
b) Prompt mode.
c) Cursor mode (Available only for certain commands).

Parameters are generally remembered by the program after each command so that a similar command issued later will use the same settings of those parameters which are not changed. This requires some caution on the part of the user. Existing settings of parameters may be determined on-line by typing the command name followed by !. The DRAW command defines regions which in this case are quadrilaterals (SHAP=Q). The corners of these regions are defined by coordinates (X1, Y1); (X2, Y2); etc. Specification of X12 means that both X1 and X2 are to be set to this value. Similarly X34 refers to X3 and X4, Y14 refers to Y1 and Y4, Y23 refers to Y2 and Y3. Regions defined by DRAW have the same dielectric properties throughout. The MATE parameter specifies whether the material has a relative permittivity of unity (MATE=0) or not (MATE=3). The permittivity is specified by the value given to AMU. Regions may have curved faces denoted by their curvatures P1 to P4. In actual fact each curved face is represented by a polygonal line.

The PE2D package uses triangular elements which can be either all three noded or all six noded. The sides of the elements are always straight lines although the potential variation will be quadratic for the six noded elements. Meshing of each region is specified within the DRAW command by the parameters N1 to N4 which denote the number of subdivisions along each face.

Boundary conditions may be:

(a) Dirichlet (fixed potential) with constant potential along the face of a region. This is denoted in the DRAW command by Fn = V, where n is the face number. The potential is set by specifying Vn.

(b) Neumann (with the normal derivative of potential specified). To denote this condition Fn is set to DV, and DVn is set to the value of the derivative (usually zero).

If an outer boundary has no assigned potential or derivative then the implied boundary condition is that of a Neumann boundary with zero normal derivative.

The command MESH checks whether the mesh is coherent. That is, whether the mesh vertices on one side of a region boundary match with those on the other side. It also generates a table of element data similar to that used (and generated) in the solver program. At the end of the mesh generation an outline of the external boundaries of the model is drawn. Any internal boundaries displayed indicate a mismatch of the mesh or region coordinates.

5.5.1 Input Data To Program

In a run with the online program there would be an interactive exchange between the program and the user, who would progressively modify his data until he was satisfied with it. The example given is really a set of streamlined input data which has already undergone this process.

Command + Parameters	Explanation
SET SYMM=AXI ELEM=LINE	Set for axisymmetric linear elements.
RECO XMIN=0 XMAX=50 YMIN=0 YMAX=50	Set picture scales.
DRAW SHAP=Q X12=1 X3=14 X4=17 Y14=0 Y23=9 P3=0.1 N1=6 N2=8 N3=6 N4=10 AMU=7 F1=V V1=1.E5 MATE=3	Define insulator regions.
DRAW X3=11 X4=14 Y14=9 Y23=18 P3=-0.1 N2=6 N4=8	
DRAW X3= 8 X4=11 Y14=18 Y23=27 P3=0.1 N2=4 N4=6	
DRAW X3= 5 X4=8 Y14=27 Y23=36 P3=-0.1 N2=3 N4=4	
DRAW X3= 2 X4=5 Y14=36 Y23=45 P3=0.1 N2=1 N4=3	
RECO MESH=YES	Redraw picture with mesh. (Figure 5.17)
RECO XMAX=80 YMAX=80	Reset scales.
DRAW X1=17 X2=14 X34=32 Y14=0 Y23=9 P1=-0.1 P3=0 N2=9 N4=7 AMU=1 F1=NO F4=V V4=0.0 MATE=0	Define air regions
DRAW X1=14 X2=11 Y14=9 Y23=18 P1=0.1 N2=11 N4=9 F4=NO	
DRAW X1=11 X2=8 Y14=18 Y23=27 P1=-0.1 N2=13 N4=11	
DRAW X1=8 X2=5 Y14=27 Y23=36 P1=0.1 N2=15 N4=13	

```
DRAW X1=5 X2=2 Y14=36 Y23=45 P1=-0.1 N2=18 N4=15

DRAW X1=2 Y14=45 Y2=46 Y3=46.5 N1=2 N3=1 N4=18
F1=V P1=0

DRAW X1=2 X2=1.414 Y1=46 Y4=46.5 Y2=47.414 Y3=48
P1=-0.5

DRAW X12=0 X3=5 X4=1.414 Y1=48 Y4=47.414 Y23=74
F1=NO F4=V V4=1.E5 N1=7 N2=1 N3=7 N4=2 P1=0 P4=-0.5

DRAW X1=1.414 X2=5 X3=60 X4=32 Y1=47.414 Y4=48 N2=11
N4=18 P4=0 F4=NO

DRAW X12=32 X34=60 Y14=0 Y2=48 Y3=74 F4=V V4=0.0
N1=32 N2=7 N3=12 N4=7

RECO
```

Redraw picture
with mesh.
(Figure 5.18)

```
DRAW X12=60 X34=200 Y14=0 Y2=74 Y3=200 F3=V
V3=0 N1=12 N2=11 N3=8 N4=11

DRAW X12=0 X3=200 X4=60 Y14=74 Y23=200
F2=V V2=0 F3=NO F4=NO N1=11 N2=8 N3=11 N4=12

RECO XMAX=200 YMAX=200
```

Redraw picture
with mesh.
(Figure 5.19)

```
MESH
N
WRITE FL=BUSH1

END
```

Generate and
test mesh.
Write file
Bush 1 to data
base.
Finish.

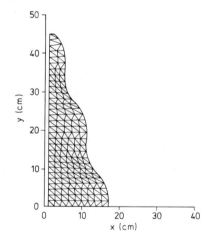

Figure 5.17   Discretization
of bush

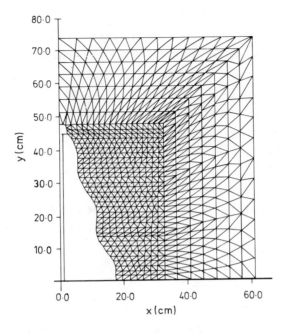

Figure 5.18   Discretization around bush

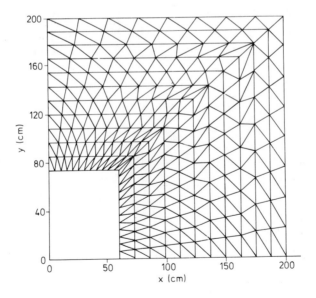

Figure 5.19   Discretization of remaining air space

72

5.5.2 Solution of Problem

The file BUSH1, which is known to the data base as BUSH1.PE2D is
now sent to the solver program. Execution time for this file on the
IBM 3081D is about 22 seconds using the conjugate gradient solver.
Core requirement is 400 k bytes. The solution is returned to the
data base as file BUSH1.RES and is then ready for the postprocessor
stage for which the pre and post processor program is again launched.
The file BUSH1.RES is read in and plots of potentials and fields
are made using the following series of commands. This package
was originally designed with magnetostatics in mind. Thus the field
components known by the program as BX, BY and BMOD are in fact
components of D, which for relative permittivity of 1 will be the
same as E.

5.5.3 Output of Results

READ FL=BUSH1.RES   Read result file.

RECO XMIN=0 XMAX=200 YMIN=0 YMAX=200   Display picture.

CONT COMP=POTE   Draw equipotential
                                                     contours.

RECO XMAX=80 YMAX=80   Redraw picture to
                                                     larger scale.

CONT   Draw equipotential
                                                     contours.

END   Finish

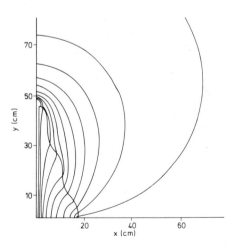

Figure 5.20   Potential
              solution
              in area
              around
              bush

It can be seen from Figure 5.20 that the sharp corner where the base of the tank meets the insulator is an area of very high field. A radius on the metal edge would reduce the electrostatic stress considerably. Another area of high field is the central conductor where a larger radius would also be beneficial. This is less important where the conductor is in the insulator but is critical at the extremity.

REFERENCES

Biddlecombe, C.S., Diserens, N.J., Riley, C.P. and Simkin, J. (1981). PE2D User Guide, (Version 6), Rutherford Appleton Laboratory, RL-81-089, December.

CHAPTER 6

Transport of
Low Conductivity Fluids

INTRODUCTION

The generation of electrostatic charge in flowing liquids rarely
causes more than a nuisance. However, when the material involved in
the charging process is of a flammable nature, the phenomenon may
become a hazard.

In 1958 Klinkenberg stated, "An analysis of case histories of
explosions ascribed to static electricity indicate where research
should start on this subject". Full-scale experimentation, he felt,
was the appropriate starting point. From such full-scale experiments
on storage tanks and aircraft re-fuelling simulations, he was able to
establish the basis of safety procedures which are followed today.
The main recommendations which he made were that:

a) Explosive vapours above volatile products should be
    avoided.

b) All metal parts close to or in contact with the
    material should be grounded.

c) The conductivity of the material should be increased
    using antistatic additive if explosive vapours could
    not be avoided.

d) If additives can not be used, and explosive vapours
    exist, then apply the usual methods of slow pumping
    or inerting.

In the process of experimentation, it has been found that results from a computer model may be used to improve the effectiveness of measurements by locating and diagnosing areas of potential hazard and experimental misinterpretation. The interaction of implementing the results derived from a computer study with those obtained from experimental measurement and interpretation makes it possible to develop models which may be applied to practical situations with some confidence.

6.1 SOURCE OF ELECTROSTATIC HAZARD

It is widely accepted that the cause of charge generation in flowing liquids is attributed to charge separation at the electric double layer which exists at the boundary between the liquid and solid surface with which it is in contact (see figure 6.1).

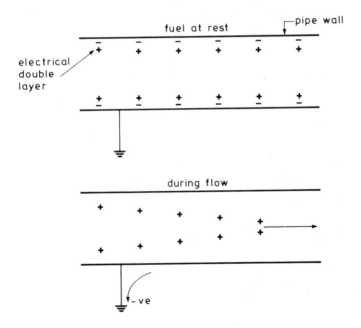

Figure 6.1   Charge separation at the electric double layer

The quantity of charge   generated in this way for different material properties and geometries, is not generally known. Even the polarity of such charge is often difficult to predict, Walmsley (1981). Several attempts have been made at such analysis. Classical electrochemistry for example yields an expression for the streaming current due to charge separation, Schon (1965), by

$$I_s = \frac{-\pi r^2 \; \varepsilon_o \varepsilon_r \; \delta p.s}{\ell \; \eta} \qquad (6.1)$$

This in general, however, fails to predict values which have been experimentally observed. Gibson and Lloyd (1970) have proposed the empirical equation (6.2) to fit experimental data which describes the streaming current in an infinitely long pipe.

$$I_s = (2r)^{-1.8} \; (v)^{1.45} + 0.01 \; 2r^{(0.4(\log 2r)x(\log v))}.K \qquad (6.2)$$

where

$$K = \frac{0.035 \; \varepsilon_r \varepsilon_o \; RTD^{0.875} \; s^{0.25}}{\mu \; F \; \eta^{0.875}}$$

which is not totally dissimilar to the results of Gavis and Kosman (1968) derived from liquid properties

$$I_s = K(v)^{1.87}.(2r)^{0.87} \qquad (6.3)$$

A more simplified approach is favoured by Schon (1965) which relates streaming current in an infinitely long pipe, to flow velocity and pipe diameter, by

$$I_s = (2r)^2 \; v^2 \; x \; 3.75 \; x \; 10^{-6} \qquad (6.4)$$

Perhaps the simplest and most general guidance available is to be found in British Standards, which relate the charge density developed to the velocity of flow for an infinite pipe by

$$\rho = 5 \; x \; 10^{-6} \; x \; v \qquad (6.5)$$

where an infinite pipe is one whose length can be expressed as

$$\ell > 3v\tau_i \qquad\qquad (6.6)$$

with

$$\tau_i = \frac{\varepsilon_r \varepsilon_o}{k} \times 10^{12}.$$

British Standards also make the obvious observation that turbulent flow produces more charge than laminar flow, the current generated in laminar flow being approximately proportional to velocity, while for turbulent flow, current is approximately proportional to velocity squared. Whichever of the above relationships is applicable, the fact remains that under certain conditions, a significant quantity of charge may be generated in flowing liquids. Furthermore, at some stage in their life, especially in fuel systems, liquids are either passed through a filter or a coalescer or both. This may have an even greater effect on charging levels due to the large surface area with which the liquid is in contact. Charge levels of up to 2000 μCm^{-3} have been reported, Gavis and Wagner (1968), for certain types of microfilter.

Having acquired a quantity of charge in transport, the liquid may then be stored for future use in a tank or similar vessel. It is this phase of the process, the storage of fuels, which will be dealt with in the following.

As a storage container is filled with charged fuel, the total charge contained, builds up. Should this accumulation lead to a discharge, then, given sufficient energy in the discharge and a combustible atmosphere, the atmosphere will ignite. It is the onset of these conditions that concerns the designer of fuelling systems.

There are at least two parameters which may give an indication of the limits of safe filling conditions. The first of these is the liquid surface potential. Strawson and Lyle (1975) suggest a value of 45 kV for the onset of hazardous discharges, which is not far removed from the value of 35 kV quoted by Kramer and Schon (1975).

Alternatively, the electric field strength at the tank roof may be used as a guide to the surface potential. This measurement has the disadvantage that it is dependent on the tank geometry, and therefore open to interpretation. One further possible hazard parameter is the input charge density. This may either be measured using relaxation chamber techniques or by assessing the field strength at the inlet. Strawson and Lyle (1975) report hazardous discharges with input charge densities as low as 20-30 μCm^{-3}. This parameter however, is highly dependent on liquid characteristics, especially conductivity, and is consequently of limited use.

6.2 EXPERIMENTAL SYSTEM STUDIED

The fuel storage facility, Diserens et al (1978), used for experimentation purposes consisted of a 2640 gallon glass-reinforced plastic (GRP) tank, with dimensions 2 m wide by 2 m long and 3 m in height. The average wall and base thickness was 0.02 m. Diesel fuel was pumped from a 6000 gallon metal storage tank through a long Cu/Ni pipe run into the GRP tank. The arrangement is shown in schematic form in Figure 6.2.

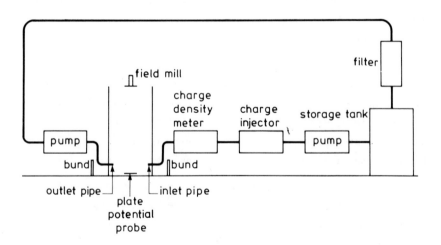

Figure 6.2   Tank and instrumentation layout

The streaming currents which were developed in the pumping process were found to be of the order of 3 μCm^{-3} and positive. It was therefore necessary to inject charge into the fuel in order to obtain significant charging levels. The monitoring of conditions in the tank itself was achieved by two different methods. Since the surface potential may be viewed as a critical hazard parameter, Strawson and Lyle (1975), it was considered to be essential that an indication of this value should be obtained by monitoring field strength at the tank roof and from calibration data the surface potential was derived. In subsequent experiments, further measurements of electrostatic conditions in the tank were made using a metal plate potential probe. This consisted of square brass plate, situated at the centre of the tank base and connected to a large metal sphere by a thin insulated wire. The potential of the sphere, and hence the potential of the metal plate and the tank base, was monitored using an electrostatic field mill mounted on an earthed plate and held a given distance from the sphere. The brass plate served a dual purpose, in that it was also used as an earthed plate when connected to ground through an ammeter. It was thus possible to simulate the earthing procedure commonly used in ships' fuel tanks.

During the experiment, measurements of fuel conductivity and temperature were also obtained. These measurements and those associated with the variation in resistivity of the GRP were conducted in accordance with BS 5958.

6.3 EXPERIMENTAL AND COMPUTATIONAL RESULTS

Computational Model: As stated previously, the mathematical problem to be undertaken is the solution of Poisson's equation for the electrostatic potential in the problem region, subject to a given charge density distribution and a prescribed set of boundary conditions.

The fuel tank was modelled as a cylinder of radius 1.0 metres and height 3 metres, as shown in Figure 6.3. A field mill (shielded to reduce sensitivity) was assumed to hang vertically on the tank axis,

80

to a height of 6 metres above the ground. The outer boundary
(corresponding to the containment bund of the GRP tank) was also
established. The boundary conditions for this axisymmetric arrangement are shown in Figure 6.4.

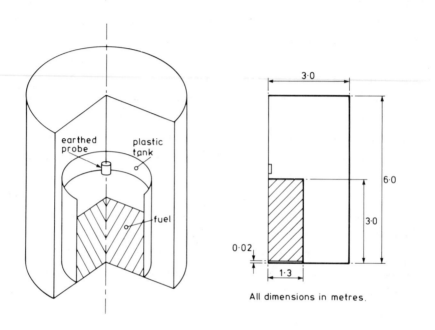

Figure 6.3   Schematic of axisymmetric tank arrangement

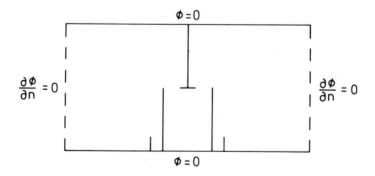

Figure 6.4   Tank model boundary conditions

Results: Initial computational assessments, based on the equivalent axisymmetric finite-element model, supported previous conclusions, Diserens et al (1978), regarding charge migration to the tank base. However, the field and potential values obtained assumed no charge leakage through the tank walls and base, and were found to be far in excess of those measured.

Measurements of the GRP conductivity were carried out to obtain an estimate of the charge lost through the tank base. Figure 6.5 illustrates the range of values obtained from various specimens of 'used' GRP tank material.

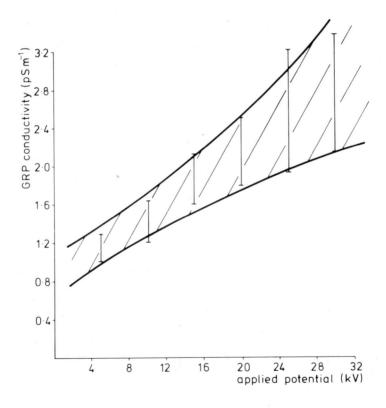

Figure 6.5 Variation of GRP conductivity with applied potential

A second series of computer evaluations was conducted with the
assumptions that charge density in the fuel was assumed constant and
that the surface charge distribution on the walls and base of the
tank was homogeneous. Using a simple Ohmic relationship, based on
average conductivity values from Figure 6.5, to assess charge leakage
through the tank base, and the principle of superposition applied to
a combination of the three charged regions(i.e. the fuel, the walls
and the base of the tank), it was possible to derive a plausible
charge distribution in the tank. The results are shown in Figure 6.6
in terms of equipotential plots for such an arrangement. Table 1
gives a summary of the conditions and potential values at each
filling level. The values of field and potential computed at the
field mill and base probe respectively are within 12 percent of the
measured values. Furthermore, the results suggest that between 10
and 15 per cent of the charge which remains in the tank is distributed
in the fuel, confirming a previous assumption, Diserens et al (1978),
made with regard to this charge distribution in the fuel. However,
both models ignore the existence of charge on the fuel surface which
in view of the computer results, Figure 6.6, is most probably due to
the existence of a vertical electrostatic field below the liquid
surface which would tend to move charge in the direction of the
surface. In the following a more detailed model taking account of
the various factors discussed is postulated.

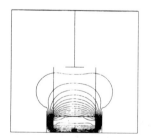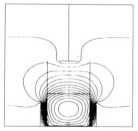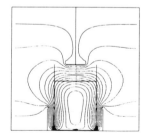

Figure 6.6 Equipotential plots for distributed charge model

Table 1

Tank Conditions and Potential Values at Each Filling Level

Figure 6.6

	a	b	c
Base Potential kV	12.7	14.7	16.5
Field at meter Vcm^{-1}	67.7	95.2	186.1
Maximum Potential kV	36.4	22.2	19.4
Contour spacing kV	2.4	1.5	1.3
Filling level m	0.75	1.50	2.25
Charge in fuel Cm^{-3}	0.28×10^{-5}	0.845×10^{-5}	0.757×10^{-6}
Charge on walls Cm^{-2}	0.32×10^{-5}	0.686×10^{-6}	0.44×10^{-7}
Charge on base Cm^{-2}	0.96×10^{-5}	0.126×10^{-4}	0.144×10^{-4}

6.3.1 Charge Migration Models

The models developed so far have all assumed charge distributions
which are uniform in the three main regions considered. The actual
charge distribution which exists depends on the input charge density,
flow rate, fuel and tank material conductivity. In addition,
turbulence plays a significant role in distributing charge evenly
throughout the fuel. Of these, input charge density and flow rate
are known to an acceptable accuracy whilst the conductivities of the
fuel and GRP are not accurately known. Computational studies indicate
that the conductivity near the fuel surface plays an important role
in the charge migration process. This, however, varies with conditions at the surface (e.g. the presence of a foam layer), and is
difficult to measure experimentally. An analysis of the effect of a
surface layer of charge is given by Klinkenberg and Van der Minne
(1958).

With these problems in mind, a model was established which allowed
charge to migrate under the influence of the electrostatic field.

Equipotential plots were obtained for gradually increasing filling
levels for a variety of surface fuel and bulk conductivities.
Combining these results it is possible to give an indication of the
conductivity values which are likely to give rise to a critical
surface potential (45 kV) for this experimental arrangement and
given streaming currents. These values are illustrated graphically
in Figure 6.7.

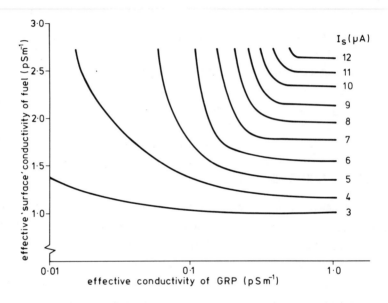

Figure 6.7   Variation of surface and tank material conductivity
with streaming current which will result in the
onset of hazardous conditions

The results which were obtained from this model, for base and
surface potential, are within 4 percent of those obtained from experiment. This substantiates the use of a formulation based on homogeneous
charge distribution to assess electrostatic conditions pertaining to
the experimental arrangement under review.

A common and effective method of reducing the charging levels in
fuel tanks is to introduce an earthed plate on the tank base.

Experimental tests were compared with a computational assessment of this condition. The charge relaxation model was adapted by imposing an earthed boundary on the tank equivalent in configuration and size to that of the actual plate used in the experiment. Any charge which migrated to this region, either from the fuel or from the tank base, was assumed to go directly to earth. The results obtained from experiment and numerical analysis are shown in Figure 6.8.

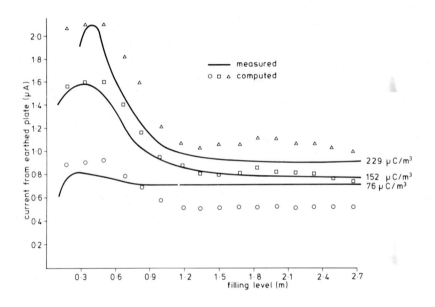

Figure 6.8   Comparison of measured and computed earth plate current

The model described in the previous section, although effective, is not sufficiently sophisticated to model situations in which homogeneous charge distributions do not occur over the regions of interest. For this reason, the charge relaxation model was extended to take account of the region and also the location within the region to which the charge relaxed. By using this approach it is possible to establish realistic non-homogeneous charge distributions.

The origins of the method are simply based on assuming an initial charge distribution at a low filling level. From this the field pattern may be calculated and the resulting charge trajectory established. The charge may then be re-distributed according to the various material conductivities. As the filling level increases, the incoming charge is superimposed homogeneously on the already established distribution in the tank. This assumption is quite reasonable due to the turbulence caused by the incoming fuel. At each increment in the filling level, charge migration is assessed and a new distribution of charge, and hence a new potential distribution,is established. The process is illustrated in Figure 6.9 which shows equipotential plots and charge migration paths for three tank filling levels. The results obtained from this model, for base and surface potential,are within 5 percent of those obtained from the charge relaxation model. This tends to indicate that the additional model complexity is not warranted for this particular simulation. However, the development of a charge migration facility within the overall model capability extends its use to those situations where the assumption of homogeneous charge distribution no longer applies.

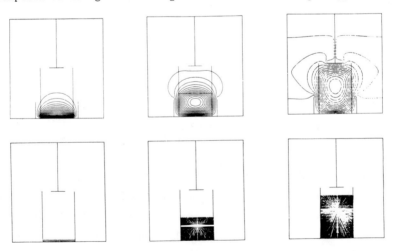

Figure 6.9   Equipotential plots and charge migration paths
from charge migration model

6.4 SHIPS TANK MODELS

The final model which is presented in this section, illustrates
the application of the finite element method to the analysis of
electrostatic conditions in real, if idealised, ships fuel tanks.
Two different tank geometries which are larger than the experimental
facility previously described, are presented. The tank shapes are
typical of those used to store fuel on small ships. The purpose of
this exercise is, in the first instance, to consider the hazard
associated with the filling the tanks, and secondly, using the
techniques which have been developed, to determine the extent to
which the results obtained from the smaller experimental facility may
be applied to different and larger tanks.

The two fuel tank configurations are illustrated in Figure 6.10.
A three-dimensional finite element model was used to calculate the
electrostatic conditions within the tanks assuming a charge density
in the fuel of 100 μCm^{-3}. Tank 1 is filled to a height of 2.3 m,
while tank 2 is filled to a height of 1.25 m. An earthed boundary is
assumed to surround the tank completely. This assumption is based on
the fact that in normal operation the tanks will be surrounded by a
good earth, namely sea water.

The resulting equipotentials for sections through the tanks
indicated in figure 6.10 are shown in figures 6.11 and 6.12. The
contours which have been obtained using this version of the finite
element program are less smooth than those obtained from previous
models. This is due to the increased complexity which accompanies
such three dimensional models, preventing such fine discretisation
as is possible with axisymmetric models. This, however, is unlikely
to detract substantially from the accuracy and reliability of the
results as the parameter of interest in this case is surface
potential. As may be seen from the equipotential plots, the surface
potential changes very little as one moves along the liquid surface,
allowing it to be modelled with a comparatively crude mesh.

The charge density which has been adopted is purely notional and

consequently the resulting potentials are far in excess of those
which could exist in reality.   In the case of tank 1, surface
potentials of the order of 1.2 MV were computed as opposed to 0.26 MV
in section 6.3 for the experimental facility for similar percentage
filling level and charge distribution.   Bearing in mind that tank 1
is of the order of 3-4 times larger than the experimental tank, it
appears that the critical hazard parameter of surface potential,
although not precisely related to tank volume, is in a similar ratio.
Similarly, tank 2 which is 2-3 times larger than the experimental
tank, has a surface potential of 650 kV as opposed to 190 kV at
similar percentage filling level and charge density.

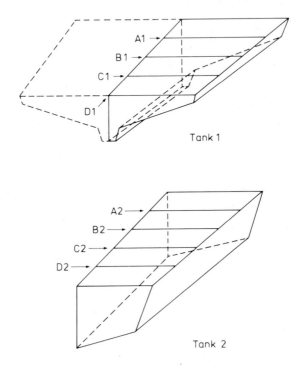

Figure 6.10   Isometric projection of typical ships fuel tanks

The charge distribution which has been assumed for this comparison is patently unrealistic. As was found in previous models, charge will inevitably relax to the tank walls and base. Nonetheless, there is no reason to suppose that a similar relationship between tank volume and surface potential for reasonably regularly shaped tanks will not hold for more complex charge distributions. Furthermore, as the charging levels in the larger tanks are likely to be lower, estimates of 'effective' conductivity are essential if realistic models are to be established.

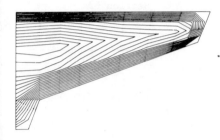

Section A1
Contour spacing 115 kV

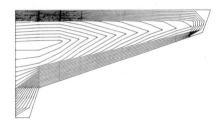

Section B1
Contour spacing 110 kV

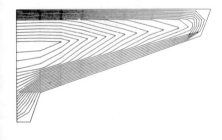

Section C1
Contour spacing 85 kV

Section D1
Contour spacing 115 kV

Figure 6.11   Equipotential plots for ships fuel tanks

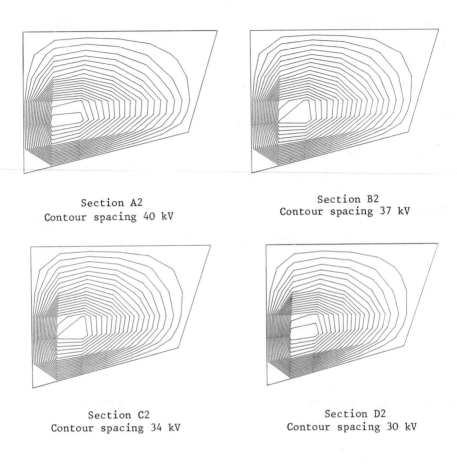

Section A2
Contour spacing 40 kV

Section B2
Contour spacing 37 kV

Section C2
Contour spacing 34 kV

Section D2
Contour spacing 30 kV

Figure 6.12   Equipotential plots of ship fuel tank

6.5 DISCUSSION

The development of finite element software to assess the electrostatic conditions in fuel tanks is, to a large extent, an interactive
process. Experimentation provides information on the behaviour and
migration of charge within such tanks, and allows progressively more
accurate computational models to be established. Computational
evaluations assist in the assessment of realistic charge distributions

which relate to a possible hazard. This process provides feedback to the experimentalist, allowing improvements to be made to the test facility, suggesting measurements that should be made, and also providing the basis of extrapolation to situations which could not be investigated experimentally because of the possible hazard or lack of access.

Computational modelling has shown that the field values obtained are far less than those to be expected if the tank was behaving as a perfect insulator. This leads to the conclusion that charge is relaxing to earth through either the tank base or the filling pipe or possibly both. Further experimental observations include the rising field values at the tank roof after filling has ceased. This is attributed to charge continuing to migrate to the fuel surface. In addition, it is apparent that surface potential is at a maximum soon after filling has commenced and then rapidly decreases as the filling level increases, rising only slightly after filling has ceased. The magnitude of the increase in surface potential after filling has ceased is not in itself significant when compared to the high surface potentials found during the early stages of filling in terms of hazard assessment.

Base potential measurements indicate a considerable migration of charge to the tank base in the early stages of filling, establishing a base potential which only increases slightly as the filling level increases. This may be readily interpreted as an equilibrium being established with charge migrating to the base at virtually the same rate as the charge migration through the base.

The insertion of an earthed plate on the tank base has proved to be an effective means of removing charge from the fuel. Typically 40% and up to 65% of the input charge can be removed in this manner during pumping. This charge drainage is especially effective and indeed desirable at early stages in the filling process since this is potentially the most hazardous period. The earth plate in these experiments was sited in the centre of the tank base since this is the region to which the majority of charge will migrate, as may be seen from the equipotential plots. In alternative tank geometries, this may not always be the case, and consequently each situation must be considered individually.

Although the experimental work has given indications of the migration and location of charge within the fuel, the exact quantity of charge in any one region is exceptionally difficult to assess or measure. Previous estimates such as those proposed by Diserens et al (1978) of 90% on the base and 10% in the fuel, have been shown to be too simplistic. The charge migration and charge relaxation models are useful in determining these values. They also serve to highlight the changing values of 'effective' fuel surface and bulk conductivities which exist throughout the tests. These can be justified by the high degree of turbulence in the early stages combined with a foam layer which exists on the fuel surface, both of which will effectively decrease the fuel conductivity. Turbulence will tend to overcome the electrostatic forces in the fuel and inhibit charge migration to the base and fuel surface. The foam layer will provide a high resistivity covering on the fuel surface thus decreasing conductivity along it. As the filling level increases, however, the foam layer gradually disperses and the level of turbulence decreases, thus leading to increase the conductivities.

The fundamental point which must be made is that the computational work suggests that the critical conductivity value is not the fuel bulk conductivity but rather the fuel surface conductivity. It is this parameter which dictates the rate at which charge migrates from the fuel surface, and to a certain extent to the fuel surface, thus largely determining the critical hazard parameter of surface potential.

As has already been stated, 'effective' fuel conductivity changes with charging levels. This factor allows the apparent non-linear relationship between the input charge density and the resulting fields and potentials to be explained. For example, superposition suggests that doubling the input charge density will double the resulting fields and potentials, given constant conductivities. This may readily be shown not to be the case from the results obtained

experimentally. The best indication of the values of these conductivities is to be found in the earth plate relaxation models and
experimental results. The fraction of the input charge relaxing to
earth through the earthed plate was experimentally observed to
increase with lower charging levels. This suggests higher fuel
conductivities allowing more rapid migration of the charge from the
fuel and indeed the base to the earthed plate. The values obtained
for these conductivities were consistent with the relationship
proposed by Britton (1980). Such an analysis, however, encounters the
difficulty of accounting for the mutual dependence of conductivity
and charge density which leads to a complex time dependent model.
This difficulty is overcome by assuming a simple variation of
conductivity over the filling process of gradually increasing
conductivity.

Despite these complications, general guidelines for safe filling
of such a re-fuelling facility may be proposed. Since the critical
stage of the filling process occurs at early filling levels, this is
the period which must be studied most carefully. Computer assessments
have suggested that at the 'norm' input charge density of 152 μCm^{-3}
'effective' fuel surface conductivity is of the order of a thirtieth
of its rest value and GRP conductivity is approximately half its rest
value (measured at the observed base voltage). Using these guidelines
and the graph shown in Figure 6.7 critical streaming currents in the
fuel may be obtained. The conductivity values may be equally adjusted
for different input charge densities by applying the relationship
established by Britton (1980).

To summarise, computation used interactively with experimentation
can lead to a better understanding of the process. The behaviour of
charge entrained in the fuel that is pumped into an insulated
container is better understood and charge migration patterns may be
derived that give feasible results which perhaps go some way to
providing guidelines for the safe filling of tanks.

94

REFERENCES

British Standards Institute. Control of undesirable static electricity, Part 1.

Britton, L.G. (1980). RDF effective relaxation as a function of charge density, (Southampton University), Unpublished.

Diserens, N.J., Smith, J.R., Bright, A.W. (1978). A preliminary study of the electric field problems in plastic tanks and their theoretical modelling by means of finite difference computer program, Journal of Electrostatics, 5, 169-182.

Gavis, J., Wagner, J.P. (1968). Electric charge generation during flow of hydrocarbons through microporous media, Chemical Engineering Science, 23, 381-391.

Gibson, N., Lloyd, F.C. (1970). Electrification of toluene flowing in large metal pipes, Journal of Physics (D), 3, 563.

Klinkenberg, A., Van Der Minne, J.L. (1958). Electrostatics in the petroleum industry, Elsevier (Amsterdam).

Kramer, H. Schon, G. (1975). Estimation of space charge and held strength in tanks during top filling with electrostatically chargeable fuels, World Petroleum Congress (Tokyo).

Schon, G., Fretag, H.H. (1965). Handbuch der Raumexplosionen, Verlag Chemie, Weinheim.

Smith J.R., Lees, P., McAllister, D. and Hughes, J. (1983). Experimental and numerical investigation of field conditions associated with the transport of low conductivity liquids and powders, Proc. IEE., 130, Pt. A, (7), 369-379.

Strawson, H., Lyle, A.R. (1975). Safe charge densities for road and rail tank car filling, Institute of Physics Conference Series, No. 27, 276-289.

Walmsley, H., Woodford, G. (1981). The polarity of the current generated by the laminar flow of a dielectric liquid, Journal of Electrostatics, 10, 283-288.

CHAPTER 7
Transport of
Low Conductivity Powders

INTRODUCTION

The generation of static electricity by pneumatic transport of low
conductivity particulate matter is a well known but little understood
phenomenon. The consequences of such charge generation can however
be hazardous in an industrial environment where pneumatic transport
systems are commonly used; for instance in the food or chemical
industries where insulating powders are transferred at high rates
into large storage silos. Published information concerning charge
accumulation and resulting electric field distribution is scant.
In this chapter, the previously described numerical techniques, are
applied to the silo problem to demonstrate means by which plausible
charge distributions and boundary conditions may be obtained.
Furthermore the method may be used to obtain a potential map and to
estimate the probable onset of hazardous conditions.

7.1 ELECTROSTATIC CONDITIONS IN SILOS

When insulating particulate matter is being pumped into silos,
frictional charging of the particles moving along the walls of the
delivery pipes (whether insulating or conducting) can lead to
significant charge accumulation within the silo even when the silo is
an earthed system, since the decay of charge to earth may be prevented
by the low conductivity of the powder, or for some powders of high
conductivity, by the insulating air medium. Under certain conditions
the existence of this charge accumulation within the silo can lead to

a hazardous situation. If the leakage of charge is comparatively small, high electric fields can result, which may reach the breakdown voltage of air and a spark of sufficient energy may be produced where the composition of the dust/air mixture is within the explosive limits of the material.

Some of the problems and dangers in these areas are documented by Bright (1977) and Maurer (1979). However, it appears that there are three important regions which can present electrostatic hazards within the silo. These are:

1) the region of the inlet pipe;

2) the bulk powder surface;

3) the air space at the top of the silo.

In the latter region there is some evidence that bipolar charging can occur and there is some unconfirmed evidence that cloud to cloud discharges might occur between the fines and the falling coarses powder. The charging process associated with the loading of a silo is complex and not completely understood at the present time. Nevertheless, in view of the considerable cost of constructing test silos it is considered a worthwhile exercise to examine the contribution that mathematical models can make towards ensuring the safe design of silos and their associated powder handling systems.

7.2 ANALYTICAL CONSIDERATIONS

At a first assessment the analysis associated with the transport of low-conductivity powders appears to be similar to the analysis of electrostatic charging of liquids. Both situations are governed by Poisson's equation, Lees et al (1980), and similar critical parameters may be applied to each. One of the principal differences lies in the resistivities of the two different types of material. Powdered materials which are considered to be hazardous, have in general a much higher resistivity than their liquid counterparts. Being

particulate in nature, it is much more difficult for charge to move
from particle to particle and hence relax to earth. This results
in a much more 'static' field being maintained in powders. This
'static' field, however, exists only until breakdown occurs. Breakdown or discharge may be low level and hence harmless, or energetic
and incendive. Low level discharge in powder systems is often
desirable as it is one of the few means by which powder may be
rapidly discharged.

As a consequence it is difficult to predict, using analytical
methods, electrostatic conditions for powder containers. Furthermore, charging levels generated in powder transport is a little
investigated subject. The charging of any pneumatically transported
powder is largely dependent on particle size distribution, pumping
velocity, powder density, geometry of pumping apparatus, humidity,
resistivity, and temperature. One of the aims of the present
chapter is to establish to what extent results obtained from small
scale experiments can be applied to full-scale silo installations
and to establish the requirements and validity of numerical models
of such arrangements.

7.3 EXPERIMENTAL OBSERVATIONS

A general investigation of powder charging is well beyond the
scope of this book. However, prior to applying the developed
numerical techniques to practical storage installations it is
necessary to conduct a series of basic experiments to establish some
of the properties of the powder under consideration. In addition,
a small scale pumping experiment is described in which the electrostatic charging and electrostatic conditions of a sample powder were
investigated.

7.3.1 Particle Size Distribution

A number of samples, each weighing 100 g, were randomly selected
from a stock of high density polyethylene powder (HDP). These
samples were then sieved using a logarithmically based series of sand

sieves with mesh sizes 1,000, 850, 710, 600, 500, 425, 355, 250, 180
and 106 μm. The resulting cumulative values for particle size
against percentage weight are given in Figure 7.1. As indicated from
this figure, 76% by weight of the powder lies between 425 and 1,000 μm
particle diameter. Among the 12.6%, which have particle size greater
than 1,000 μm, are large malformed particles which have, presumably,
been inadequately ground. The results obtained for the groups below
425 μm are especially susceptible to error due to the ease with
which these particles may be charged. As the sieving process itself
involves agitation, the smaller particles tend to acquire static
charge and adhere to other particles or to the sieves. The particu-
larly low values for percentage weight of the smaller particles may
therefore be due to the difficulty involved in separating them from
the larger species.

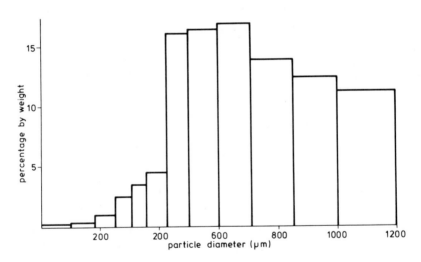

Figure 7.1   Particle size distribution (HDP)

7.3.2 Charge/Mass Ratio

The maximum charge/mass ratio which may be sustained by a spherical
particle before breakdown of the surrounding air occurs, may be
readily derived, Blythe and Reddish (1974).

$$\frac{q_m}{M} = \frac{3\ E_b\ \varepsilon_o}{r\ D}$$ (7. 1)

Assuming a material density of 950 kgm^{-3} for HDP particle, Kaye and Laby (1974), in the range 0–1,000 μm, the theoretical charge mass ratio is given by curve 1 in Figure 7.2. Blythe and Reddish (1979) suggest a more practical value as being 0.376 of the maximum value, which is given by curve 2, Figure 7.2.

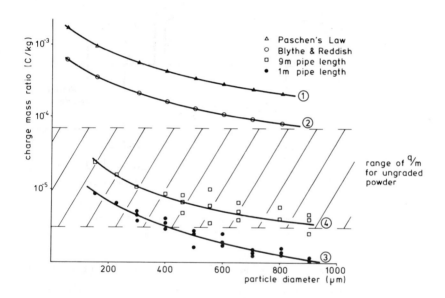

Figure 7.2   Charging Characteristic (HDP)

Two experiments were performed on the various cuts of powder obtained from the above particle size analysis in an attempt to obtain values for charge/mass ratio which were developed under certain transportation conditions.

Small quantities (between 10 and 25 g depending on particle size) of HDP powder were pneumatically transported along a one metre length of polythene piping of internal diameter 25 mm. The powder was

pumped into a Faraday cup seated on a nylon base. The Faraday cup
was connected to earth through an electrometer. The overall experimental arrangement is shown in Figure 7.3.

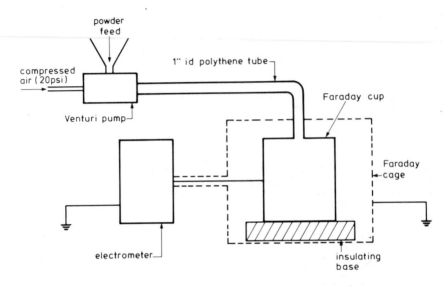

Figure 7.3   Schematic arrangement for charge/mass
ratio measurement

The charge/mass ratio which resulted from the pumping process was
calculated from the mass of powder which was transported and the
mirror current to earth, integrated to give charge by the electrometer. The results which were obtained are shown in Figure 7.2,
curve 3.

As may be seen, the results are consistent in terms of relative
value but approximately 100 times less than the maximum expected value
of q/m. In the effort to obtain higher charging values, a 9 metre
section of piping was substituted for the one metre length. Further
runs were done for the same particulate size bands, and the charge/
mass ratio calculated in the same manner. The results for this

experiment are plotted on curve 4, figure 7.2. Again the shape of the curve is consistent with the maximum expected value and the magnitude is 4 times greater than for the short pipe length. Further charge/mass ratio measurements were done for ungraded powder samples using a higher transport velocity. The range of charge mass ratios obtained is shown by the shaded area in Figure 7.2, the values lying between 3 and 80 μCkg^{-1}.

Although the results obtained for charge/mass ratio measurements for various conditions cover a wide range of values, a consistent trend was observed, especially for the graded powder samples. The longer the pipework system through which the powder is transported, and the higher the transport velocity, the higher the charging levels. As expected, the maximum charging levels obtained in the experimental arrangements were not of the same magnitude as the theoretical maxima. This may be due to the assumptions which were made in deriving the maximum charging levels, namely that the particles were spherical, which they patently are not,and that no low level discharge, such as corona, may discharge the powder. Furthermore, no attempt was made to enhance the charging conditions, i.e. to increase the transport velocity or increase the pipe length, beyond the initial choice used in the experiments, in order to ascertain if the charging could be increased in this way. Another factor which has been ignored is the possible existence of bipolar charging which would reduce the net value of charge/mass ratio.

Nonetheless the experiments gave a working assessment of the charge/mass ratio which may be expected for the particular powder transport system used. This in turn may be used in future assessment of the field conditions which may exist in such storage containers.

7.3.3 Powder Density Measurement

The density of solid HDP has been quoted by Kaye and Laby (1974) as 940-965 kg/m³. The density of powdered HDP will obviously be less, and largely dependent on compaction. It is necessary therefore to obtain an estimate of the bulked density in order to

obtain charge density values from charge/mass ratio measurements.
As most of the situations in which the powder is used in small scale
experiments involve little or no compaction, this factor has been
ignored. The powder density was obtained by loading a container of
known volume and weighing the volume of powder which it contained.
Over a series of measurements a value was found for the density of
unpacked HDP of 550 kg/m³ .

7.4 PRACTICAL APPLICATION OF EXPERIMENTATION AND ANALYSIS

The applicability of the results obtained from small scale
experiments to large scale facilities is difficult to assess.
Patently, full scale storage containers such as silos, are susceptible to external influences not experienced in laboratory conditions.
Humidity and temperature in particular vary substantially in the
full scale situation, whilst the laboratory scale experiment is
usually free from such influences. Furthermore the increased scale
of such facilities prevents accurate control and observation of the
filling process. As a consequence, the conclusions which may be
drawn from small scale work, with regard to full scale facilities,
may only be tentative without confirmatory experimental data from
the full scale situation.

Such a tentative model was established for a test silo. An
axisymmetric finite element program was used to model the experimental silo shown in Figure 7.4. Figure 7.5 shows the mesh arrangement and the nature of the problem studied. HDP powder was assumed
to flow vertically downwards and heap with an angle of repose of
45 degrees. The dielectric constant of the powder was taken to be
2.0 and the charge densities of bulk powder and fines were assumed
to be identical to those derived by Lees et al (1982).

Equipotential plots were obtained for various filling levels as
shown on Figure 7.6 and the maximum field at the powder/fines
interface calculated. The results obtained suggest that the breakdown strength of air is exceeded soon after the 0.5 metre filling
level is reached. These estimates quite obviously make considerable

assumptions with regard to the electrostatic conditions within the silo. The analysis ignores the possible existence of low level discharge due to local field intensification and also assumes that charge densities similar to those realised in the small scale experiment exist in the large scale. As these assumptions are likely to give an overestimate of the conditions which exist in practical silos, they are perhaps justifiable.

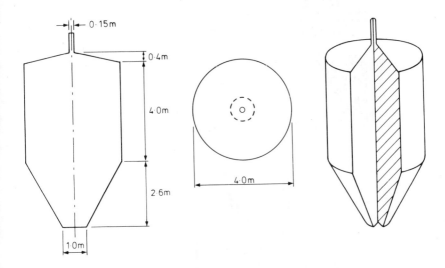

Figure 7.4   Practical configuration of silo

The situation portrayed here is a mathematical idealisation. The practical situation is not so simple. High charge densities in the inlet pipe can lead to sparking in that area. This will reduce the overall charge density of the bulk powder. Again localised sparking and corona discharge complicate the situation. Nevertheless, it is contended that the methods outlined in this chapter give a greater insight into the practical problem and that, if used in conjunction with further experimentation, can lead to more sophisticated and useful mathematical formulations which take account of discharges and non-homogeneous charge distributions.

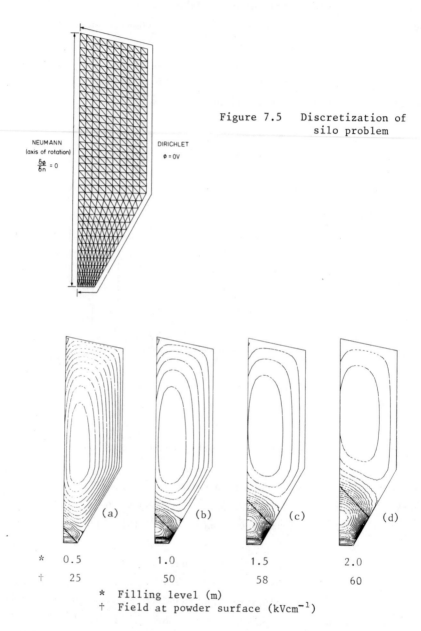

Figure 7.5   Discretization of
             silo problem

* Filling level (m)
† Field at powder surface (kVcm⁻¹)

Figure 7.6   Equipotential plots for various filling levels

REFERENCES

Blythe, A.R. and Reddish, E. (1979). Charge on powders and bulking effects. Inst. Phys. Conf. Ser. No. 48, 107-114.

Bright, A.W. (1977). Electrostatic hazards in liquids and powders. Journal of Electrostatics, 4, 131-147.

Kaye, G.W.C. and Laby, T.M. (1974). Tables of physical and chemical constants. Longman, 14th edn., 252.

Lees, P., Bright, A.W., Smith, J.R., Diserens, N.J. and McAllister, D. (1980). The finite element method applied to axisymmetric field problems in silos. IEEE Transactions on Industrial Applications, IA-16, (6), 749-754.

Lees, P., McAllister, D. and Smith, J.R. (1982). An experimental and computational study of electrostatic fields arising during the pumping of powder into small metal and plastic containers. IEEE (IAS) Conf. Record, 1167-1171.

Maurer, B. (1979). Discharges due to electrostatic charging of particles in large storage silos. German Chemical Engineering, 4, 189-195.

APPENDIX A

Shape Functions for Use with Finite Elements (including surface integral methods)

A1 ONE DIMENSIONAL SHAPE FUNCTIONS

Two node line element.

$$N_1 = \frac{1 - \xi}{2}$$

$$\xi = -1 \qquad \xi = +1$$

$$N_2 = \frac{1 + \xi}{2}$$

$$N_1 \qquad\qquad N_2$$

Three node line element.

$$N_1 = \frac{\xi(\xi - 1)}{2}$$

$$\xi = -1 \qquad \xi = 0 \qquad \xi = +1$$

$$N_2 = \frac{(1 - \xi)(1 + \xi)}{2}$$

$$N_1 \qquad\qquad N_3 \qquad\qquad N_2$$

$$N_3 = \frac{\xi(\xi + 1)}{2}$$

A2 TWO DIMENSIONAL SHAPE FUNCTIONS

The shape functions for a 3 node triangular element, at a point given by the normalised area coordinates (L1, L2, L3), are:

$$N_i = L_i$$

where L is the coordinate with value 1 at node i.

For the 6 node triangular element:

for corner nodes $N_i = (2L_i - 1)L_i$

where L_i is the coordinate with value 1 at node i.

for mid side nodes $N_i = 4L_1 L_2$

where L_1 and L_2 are the coordinates which have value $\frac{1}{2}$ at node i.

For the 4 node rectangular element the shape functions at a point given by normalised cartesian coordinates ξ and η are:

$$N_i = \frac{1}{4} (1 + \xi\xi_i)(1 + \eta\eta_i)$$

where (ξ_i, η_i) are the coordinates of node i.

For the 8 node rectangular element:

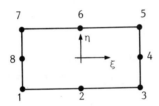

for corner nodes

$$N_i = \frac{1}{4} (1 + \xi\xi_i)(1 + \eta\eta_i)(\xi\xi_i + \eta\eta_i - 1)$$

for mid side nodes

where $\xi_i = 0$ $\qquad N_i = \frac{1}{2}(1 - \xi^2)(1 + \eta\eta_i)$

where $\eta_i = 0$ $\qquad N_i = \frac{1}{2}(1 - \eta^2)(1 + \xi\xi_i).$

A3 THREE DIMENSIONAL SHAPE FUNCTIONS

For the 8 node 'brick' element:

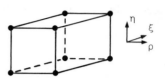

$$N_i = \frac{1}{8} (1 + \xi\xi_i)(1 + \eta\eta_i)(1 + \rho\rho_i)$$

where (ξ_i, η_i, ρ_i) are the coordinates of node i.

For the 20 node 'brick' element:

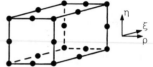

for corner nodes:

$$N_i = \frac{1}{8} (1 + \xi\xi_i)(1 + \eta\eta_i)(1 + \rho\rho_i)(\xi\xi_i + \eta\eta_i + \rho\rho_i - 2)$$

for mid edge nodes:

where $\xi_i = 0$ $N_i = \frac{1}{4} (1 - \xi^2)(1 + \eta\eta_i)(1 + \rho\rho_i)$

where $\eta_i = 0$ $N_i = \frac{1}{4} (1 - \eta^2)(1 + \xi\xi_i)(1 + \xi\xi_i)$

where $\rho = 0$ $N_i = \frac{1}{4} (1 - \rho^2)(1 + \xi\xi_i)(1 + \eta\eta_i)$

For prism elements, area coordinates are assumed in planes parallel to the triangular faces and cartesian coordinates in the transverse direction.

6 node prism.

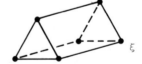

$$N_i = \frac{1}{2} L_i(1 + \xi\xi_i)$$

where L_i is the area coordinate with value 1 at node i and ξ_i is the value of ξ at node i.

15 node prism:

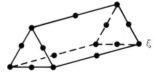

for corner nodes:

$$N_i = \tfrac{1}{2}L_i(2L_i - 1)(1 + \xi\xi_i)\xi\xi_i$$

for mid nodes of triangular ends:

$$N_i = 2L_1L_2(1 + \xi\xi_i)\xi\xi_i$$

where L_1 and L_2 are the coordinates with value $\tfrac{1}{2}$ at N_i.

The derivatives of the shape functions with respect to the normalised coordinates may be obtained by differentiation of the above equations.

For triangular area coordinates two independent variables are required. This is achieved by making the substitutions:

$$L_1 = \xi, \qquad L_2 = \eta, \qquad L_3 = 1 - \xi - \eta$$

The derivatives with respect to these are then used to form the Jacobian.

110

APPENDIX B
Some Useful Numerical Integration Formulae

B1 GAUSSIAN QUADRATURE (ONE-DIMENSIONAL)

$$\int f(x)dx = \sum_{i=1}^{n} W_i \cdot f(a)$$

For quadrilaterals the formulae need to be applied in 2 directions.

For cuboids (brick elements) the formulae need to be applied in three directions.

Order	Number of Points	a	Weights
2	2	0.5773502691896	1.0
3	3	0.7745966692415 0.0	0.5555555555556 0.8888888888889
4	4	0.8611363115941 0.3399810435849	0.3478548451375 0.6521451548625

B2 TRIANGULAR ELEMENTS

$$\int f(L, M, N) \cdot dA = \sum_{i=1}^{n} W_i \cdot f(I, J, K)$$

Order	Number of Points	Area coordinates	Weights
1	1	0.3333333333333 0.3333333333333 0.3333333333333	1.0
2	3	0.6666666666667 0.1666666666667 0.1666666666667	0.3333333333333
3	6	0.6590276223741 0.2319333685530 0.1090390090729	0.1666666666667

Note: The required number of integrating points is obtained by permutation of the 3 area coordinates.

APPENDIX C
Computer Coding

C1 PROGRAM STRUCTURE

A simple FORTRAN program is listed which will solve 2D axisymmetric
finite element problems. The coding is essentially identical to
that which was used to solve many of the illustrative examples in
this book. It is not the intention that the program should be seen
as a definitive finite element program, but merely a starting point
from which the beginner may develop his own techniques.

The program is structured in 6 sections.

C2 MAIN PROGRAM

All input data required to define the problem is read from a
data file. The program then calls subroutine CALC which constructs
the matrix A and column vector B. CALL FORCE, modifies A and B to
take account of fixed potential (Dirichlet) boundary conditions.
CALL SOLVE finds the solution to the equation Ax = B. Finally the
nodal coordinates and potentials are output to a data file. All data
transfer between main program and subroutines is done using five
common blocks. SHAPE contains the problem geometry; X and Y
coordinates, connectivity array, number of nodes, number of triangles
and the matrix bandwidth. LOCAL contains the X and Y coordinates and
local arrays which pertain to a given triangle. This common block
is updated as the global matrix is constructed and is modified only
in the LOC and CALC subroutines. OUT contains the 'rectangularised'

A matrix and the B vector (which holds the potential solution once SOLVE has been run). DIRIC contains the fixed potential or Dirichlet conditions for each nodal point and the dielectric constant for each triangle. CDEN contains the information relating to charge distribution. ICDS contains a flag for each triangle indicating if a surface charge is required, the value being held in CDIST, while CD contains space charge values.

C3 CALC - GLOBAL MATRIX ASSEMBLER

The subroutine initialises the rectangular 'A matrix' S, and the B vector to zero. Then considering each triangle in turn, it assigns the details of triangle geometry to XP and YP which are used by LOC and SURF. These routines, which are described later, establish the local matrix for each triangle taking account of space and surface charge. The local matrix derived for each triangle stored in SML and BL is then assembled in the global arrays S and B.

C4 LOC - LOCAL MATRIX ASSEMBLER

This subroutine which is called from CALC for each triangle, initialises the local array S and vector B. The triangle area XAREA and centroid R are calculated. The local S matrix is then constructed using the Universal Matrix technique (Silvester 1978), space charge effects being included in the B vector.

C5 SURF - SURFACE CHARGE EFFECTS

If a charge is assigned to the side of a triangle this routine is invoked. The value of charge distribution is contained in CDIST. Depending on which side the charge is to be assigned (fixed by ICDS), the two relevant locations of the B vector are modified.

C6 FORCE - DIRICHLET CONDITIONS

The subroutine checks each node in turn. If the relevant location of DIR array is set to 1.0×10^{37} no action is taken. Otherwise a row and column of the S array are deleted and the value of the nodal potential set at the value indicated by the relevant location in the DIR array.

C7   SOLVE - MATRIX EQUATION SOLVER

This subroutine solves the matrix equation:

Ax = b

The A matrix is in a rectangular form and is decomposed to an upper triangular matrix using Gaussian elimination. A solution, which is located in the B vector, is then obtained by back substitution. This routine is similar to that given in Segerlind (1976).

C8   RUNNING THE PROGRAM

A simple mesh for the problem posed by Asano (1977) is shown along with the required input data to define the problem. (Figure C.1).

The program will read in the above data and then calculate the local array for each triangle. (Note for triangles which contain no space charge the B vector entries are zero and that in all cases the local A matrix is symmetrical.)

The local values are assembled to give the rectangular S matrix and B vector shown in Figure C.2. (Note for example that on the first row the first entry is 0.511, the sum of the (1,1) locations of local arrays 1 and 2 (0.461 + 0.050), the only triangles containing node 1.)

The assembled matrix then has Dirichlet conditions forced. In this case all the Dirichlet values are zero. (See Figure C.3). These may be identified by a 1.0 in the first column of the S array and a 0.0 in the B array.

Finally, the problem is solved to yield the potential solution given in figure C.4.

```
ASANO PROBLEM
20   24    6
 1    0.0     0.0      0.0E+01
 2    0.33    0.0      0.0E+01
 3    0.66    0.0      0.0E+01
 4    1.0     0.0      0.0E+01
 5    0.0     0.5      1.0E+38
 6    0.33    0.5      1.0E+38
 7    0.66    0.5      1.0E+38
 8    1.0     0.5      0.0E+01
 9    0.0     1.0      1.0E+38
10    0.33    1.0      1.0E+38
11    0.66    1.0      1.0E+38
12    1.0     1.0      0.0E+01
13    0.0     1.5      1.0E+38
14    0.33    1.5      1.0E+38
15    0.66    1.5      1.0E+38
16    1.0     1.5      0.0E+01
17    0.0     2.0      0.0E+01
18    0.33    2.0      0.0E+01
19    0.66    2.0      0.0E+01
20    1.0     2.0      0.0E+01
 1    2    6   0   0.0    0.00001   2.0
 1    6    5   0   0.0    0.00001   2.0
 2    3    7   0   0.0    0.00001   2.0
 2    7    6   0   0.0    0.00001   2.0
 3    4    8   0   0.0    0.00001   2.0
 3    8    7   0   0.0    0.00001   2.0
 5    6   10   0   0.0    0.00001   2.0
 5   10    9   0   0.0    0.00001   2.0
 6    7   11   0   0.0    0.00001   2.0
 6   11   10   0   0.0    0.00001   2.0
 7    8   12   0   0.0    0.00001   2.0
 7   12   11   0   0.0    0.00001   2.0
 9   10   14   0   0.0    0.0       1.0
 9   14   13   0   0.0    0.0       1.0
10   11   15   0   0.0    0.0       1.0
10   15   14   0   0.0    0.0       1.0
11   12   16   0   0.0    0.0       1.0
11   16   15   0   0.0    0.0       1.0
13   14   18   0   0.0    0.0       1.0
13   18   17   0   0.0    0.0       1.0
14   15   19   0   0.0    0.0       1.0
14   19   18   0   0.0    0.0       1.0
15   16   20   0   0.0    0.0       1.0
15   20   19   0   0.0    0.0       1.0
```

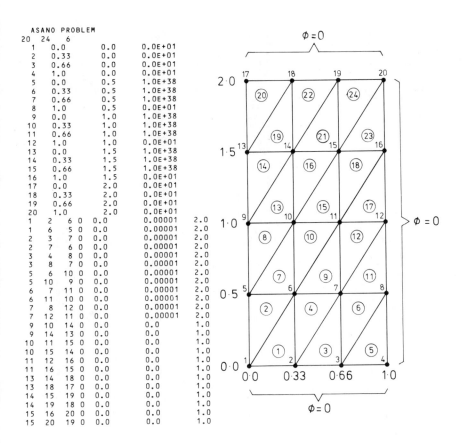

Figure C1   Input Data for 'Asano' Problem

REFERENCES

Asano, K. (1977). Electrostatic potential and field in a cylindrical tank containing charged liquid, Proc. IEE, Vol. 124, No. 12.

Segerlind, L.J. (1976). Applied finite element analysis, Wiley.

Silvester, P. (1978). Construction of triangular finite element universal matrices, Int. J. Num. Methods in Eng., Vol. 12, pp 237-244.

ASSEMBLED S MATRIX AND B VECTOR

0.511	-0.461	0.000	0.000	-0.050	0.000	8855.0
4.344	-2.880	0.000	0.000	-1.004	0.000	99176.2
13.954	-7.264	0.000	0.000	-3.810	0.000	325796.5
10.623	0.000	0.000	0.000	-3.359	0.000	163124.5
0.676	-0.576	0.000	0.000	-0.050	0.000	10626.0
7.306	-4.723	0.000	0.000	-1.004	0.000	148764.3
25.132	-12.790	0.000	0.000	-3.810	0.000	546126.3
19.508	0.000	0.000	0.000	-3.359	0.000	455306.3
0.421	-0.346	0.000	0.000	-0.025	0.000	1771.0
5.134	-3.283	0.000	0.000	-0.502	0.000	49588.1
18.155	-9.158	0.000	0.000	-1.905	0.000	220329.8
14.197	0.000	0.000	0.000	-1.679	0.000	292181.8
0.338	-0.288	0.000	0.000	-0.025	0.000	0.0
3.653	-2.361	0.000	0.000	-0.502	0.000	0.0
12.566	-6.395	0.000	0.000	-1.905	0.000	0.0
9.754	0.000	0.000	0.000	-1.679	0.000	0.0
0.083	-0.058	0.000	0.000	0.000	0.000	0.0
1.481	-0.922	0.000	0.000	0.000	0.000	0.0
5.589	-2.763	0.000	0.000	0.000	0.000	0.0
4.442	0.000	0.000	0.000	0.000	0.000	0.0

Figure C2

S MATRIX AND B VECTOR WITH DIRICHLET CONDITIONS

1.000	0.000	0.000	0.000	0.000	0.000	0.0
1.000	0.000	0.000	0.000	0.000	0.000	0.0
1.000	0.000	0.000	0.000	0.000	0.000	0.0
1.000	0.000	0.000	0.000	0.000	0.000	0.0
0.676	-0.576	0.000	0.000	-0.050	0.000	10626.0
7.306	-4.723	0.000	0.000	-1.004	0.000	148764.3
25.132	0.000	0.000	0.000	-3.810	0.000	546126.3
1.000	0.000	0.000	0.000	0.000	0.000	0.0
0.421	-0.346	0.000	0.000	-0.025	0.000	1771.0
5.134	-3.283	0.000	0.000	-0.502	0.000	49588.1
18.155	0.000	0.000	0.000	-1.905	0.000	220329.8
1.000	0.000	0.000	0.000	0.000	0.000	0.0
0.338	-0.288	0.000	0.000	0.000	0.000	0.0
3.653	-2.361	0.000	0.000	0.000	0.000	0.0
12.566	0.000	0.000	0.000	0.000	0.000	0.0
1.000	0.000	0.000	0.000	0.000	0.000	0.0
1.000	0.000	0.000	0.000	0.000	0.000	0.0
1.000	0.000	0.000	0.000	0.000	0.000	0.0
1.000	0.000	0.000	0.000	0.000	0.000	0.0
1.000	0.000	0.000	0.000	0.000	0.000	0.0

Figure C3

ASANO PROBLEM

NODE	X-COORD	Y-COORD	POTENTIAL
1	0.00000	0.00000	0.0000E+00
2	0.33000	0.00000	0.0000E+00
3	0.66000	0.00000	0.0000E+00
4	1.00000	0.00000	0.0000E+00
5	0.00000	0.50000	0.6602E+05
6	0.33000	0.50000	0.5490E+05
7	0.66000	0.50000	0.3631E+05
8	1.00000	0.50000	0.0000E+00
9	0.00000	1.00000	0.4790E+05
10	0.33000	1.00000	0.4268E+05
11	0.66000	1.00000	0.2814E+05
12	1.00000	1.00000	0.0000E+00
13	0.00000	1.50000	0.1289E+05
14	0.33000	1.50000	0.1097E+05
15	0.66000	1.50000	0.6326E+04
16	1.00000	1.50000	0.0000E+00
17	0.00000	2.00000	0.0000E+00
18	0.33000	2.00000	0.0000E+00
19	0.66000	2.00000	0.0000E+00
20	1.00000	2.00000	0.0000E+00

Stages in the solution of
'Asano' problem

Figure C4

C9   PROGRAM LISTING

```
C***********************************************************************
C                        COMMON DATA BLOCK                    *
C***********************************************************************
      COMMON/SHAPE/X(3000),Y(3000),IV(6000,3),NOPTL,NOTR,NBW
      COMMON/OUT/B(3000),S(3000,50)
      COMMON/LOCAL/XP(3),YP(3),SML(3,3),BL(3)
      COMMON/DIRIC/DIR(3000),DC(6000)
      COMMON/CDEN/ICDS(6000),CDIST(6000),CD(6000)
C***********************************************************************
C
      DIMENSION TITLE(10)
      OP=11
      IP=10
C
C               READ IN BASIC PROBLEM DATA
C               TITLE - PROBLEM TITLE UP TO 40 CHARACTERS
C               NOPTL - NUMBER OF NODES DEFINING PROBLEM (3000 MAX.)
C               NOTR  - NUMBER OF TRIANGLES IN PROBLEM   (6000 MAX.)
C               NBW   - BANDWIDTH OF 'STIFFNESS' MATRIX  (  50 MAX.)
C
      READ(IP,600) TITLE
  600 FORMAT(10A4)
      READ(IP,100) NOPTL,NOTR,NBW
  100 FORMAT(3I4)
C
C               READ IN NODAL INFORMATION
C               X(I)  - X COORDINATE ARRAY
C               Y(I)  - Y COORDINATE ARRAY
C               DIR(I)- DIRICHLET CONDITION ARRAY
C                       ( SET TO FORCING VALUE
C                         OR TO 1.0E38 IF UNFORCED )
C
  400 READ(IP,200) (IDUM,X(I),Y(I),DIR(I),I=1,NOPTL)
  200 FORMAT(I5,2F10.5,E12.4)
C
C               READ IN ELEMENT INFORMATION
C               IV(I,J) - THE NUMBERS OF THE NODES WHICH FORM
C                         THE ITH ELEMENT (J=1,2,3)
C               ICDS(I) - A FLAG TO INDICATE WHICH SIDE (IF ANY)
C                         HAS A SURFACE CHARGE ASSIGNED TO IT
C               CDIST(I)- SURFACE CHARGE DISTRIBUTION (C/M2)
C               CD(I)   - CHARGE DENSITY              (C/M3)
C               DC(I)   - DIELECTRIC CONSTANT
C
      READ(IP,300) ((IV(I,J),J=1,3),ICDS(I),CDIST(I),
     &              CD(I),DC(I),I=1,NOTR)
  300 FORMAT(3I4,I2,3F10.6)
C
C               CALL SUBROUTINE TO CONSTRUCT GLOBAL MATRIX
C
      CALL CALC
C
C               CALL SUBROUTINE TO FORCE DIRICHLET POINTS
C
      CALL FORCE
C
C               CALL SUBROUTINE TO SOLVE MATRIX
C
      CALL SOLVE
C
C
      WRITE(OP,600) TITLE
      WRITE(OP,700)
  700 FORMAT(/,' NODE    X-COORD   Y-COORD  POTENTIAL ',/)
      WRITE(OP,200) (I,X(I),Y(I),B(I),I=1,NOPTL)
C
      STOP
      END
```

```
      SUBROUTINE CALC
C
C**********************************************************************
C                       COMMON DATA BLOCK                            *
C**********************************************************************
      COMMON/SHAPE/X(3000),Y(3000),IV(6000,3),NOPTL,NOTR,NBW
      COMMON/LOCAL/XP(3),YP(3),SML(3,3),BL(3)
      COMMON/OUT/B(3000),S(3000,50)
      COMMON/DIRIC/DIR(3000),DC(6000)
      COMMON/CDEN/ICDS(6000),CDIST(6000),CD(6000)
C**********************************************************************
C
C           INITIALISE GLOBAL STIFFNESS  AND OUTPUT VECTORS
C
      DO10 I=1,NOPTL
      B(I)=0.0
      DO20 J=1,NBW
      S(I,J)=0.0
 20   CONTINUE
 10   CONTINUE
C
C           CALCULATE LOCAL STIFFNESS AND OUTPUT VECTORS
C           LOOP THROUGH EACH TRIANGLE ADDING THE CONTRIBUTION
C           OF EACH ELEMENT TO THE GLOBAL ARRAY
C
      DO30 IT=1,NOTR
C
C           PUT THE COORDINATES OF TRIANGLE IT INTO ARRAYS
C           XP AND YP FOR USE IN THE SUBROUTINE LOCAL
C
      IJK=3
      DO40 I=1,IJK
      ITT=IT
      XP(I)=X(IV(IT,I))
      YP(I)=Y(IV(IT,I))
 40   CONTINUE
C
C           SET UP LOCAL STIFFNESS MATRIX
C
      CALL LOC(ITT)
C
C           CHECK FOR SURFACE CHARGE
C
      IF(ICDS(ITT).EQ.0) GOTO60
      CALL SURF(ITT)
C
C           INSERT THE LOCAL FORCE VECTOR VALUES INTO
C           GLOBAL ARRAY AT APPROPRIATE INDEX
C
 60   DO50 I=1,IJK
      ITRANS=IV(IT,I)
      B(ITRANS)=B(ITRANS)+BL(I)
C
C           INSERT THE LOCAL STIFFNESS MATRIX VALUES
C           INTO GLOBAL MATRIX
C
      DO50 J=1,IJK
      JTRANS=IV(IT,J)
C
C           ONLY NECESSARY TO CONSIDER UPPER TRIANGLE
C           DUE TO SYMMETRY
C
      IF(ITRANS.GT.JTRANS) GOTO50
C
C           CALCULATE THE S ARRAY (RECTANGULAR) LOCATION
C           FROM THE GLOBAL MATRIX INDECES
C
      IJT=JTRANS-ITRANS+1
      S(ITRANS,IJT)=S(ITRANS,IJT)+SML(I,J)
```

```
      SUBROUTINE LOC(IT)
C
C*********************************************************************
C                       COMMON DATA BLOCK                            *
C*********************************************************************
      COMMON/LOCAL/X(3),Y(3),S(3,3),B(3)
      COMMON/DIRIC/DIR(3000),DC(6000)
      COMMON/CDEN/ICDS(6000),CDIST(6000),CD(6000)
C*********************************************************************
C
C          INITIALISE S AND B MATRICES
C
      DO10 I=1,3
      B(I)=0.0
      DO20 J=1,3
      S(I,J)=0.0
 20   CONTINUE
 10   CONTINUE
C
C          ESTABLISH TRIANGLE AREA AND X COORDINATE OF CENTROID
C
      R=(X(1)+X(2)+X(3))/3.0
      XAREA=0.5*(Y(2)*(X(1)-X(3))+Y(3)*(X(2)-X(1))+Y(1)*(X(3)-X(2)))
C
C   CONSTRUCT LOCAL STIFFNESS MATRIX
C
      XA=SQRT((X(2)-X(3))**2+(Y(2)-Y(3))**2)
      XB=SQRT((X(3)-X(1))**2+(Y(3)-Y(1))**2)
      XC=SQRT((X(2)-X(1))**2+(Y(2)-Y(1))**2)
      T1=(XB*XB+XC*XC-XA*XA)/(2.0*XC*XB)
      T2=(XA*XA+XC*XC-XB*XB)/(2.0*XA*XC)
      T3=(XA*XA+XB*XB-XC*XC)/(2.0*XA*XB)
      T1=SQRT(1.0/(1.0-T1*T1)-1.0)
      T2=SQRT(1.0/(1.0-T2*T2)-1.0)
      T3=SQRT(1.0/(1.0-T3*T3)-1.0)
      C1=2.0*DC(IT)*3.14159*R*R*T1/2.0
      C2=2.0*DC(IT)*3.14159*R*R*T2/2.0
      C3=2.0*DC(IT)*3.14159*R*R*T3/2.0
      S(1,1)=C2+C3
      S(1,2)=-C3
      S(1,3)=-C2
      S(2,2)=C1+C3
      S(2,3)=-C1
      S(3,3)=C1+C2
      S(2,1)=S(1,2)
      S(3,1)=S(1,3)
      S(3,2)=S(2,3)
C
C          CONSTRUCT FORCE VECTOR
C
      XFAC=CD(IT)*XAREA*2.0*3.14159*R/(8.854E-12)
      B(1)=(X(1)*2.0+X(2)+X(3))*XFAC/(12.0)
      B(2)=(X(1)+2.0*X(2)+X(3))*XFAC/(12.0)
      B(3)=(X(1)+X(2)+X(3)*2.0)*XFAC/(12.0)
C
      RETURN
      END
```

```
      SUBROUTINE SURF(IT)
C
C*****************************************************************
C                     COMMON DATA BLOCK                         *
C*****************************************************************
      COMMON/SHAPE/X(3000),Y(3000),IV(6000,3),NOPTL,NOTR,NBW
      COMMON/LOCAL/XP(3),YP(3),SML(3,3),BL(3)
      COMMON/OUT/B(3000),S(3000,50)
      COMMON/DIRIC/DIR(3000),DC(6000)
      COMMON/CDEN/ICDS(6000),CDIST(6000),CD(6000)
C*****************************************************************
C
C        MODIFY FORCE VECTOR TO TAKE ACCOUNT OF SURFACE CHARGE
C
      CTR=CDIST(IC)*2.0*3.14159/(8.854E-12)
      GOTO(10,20,30),ICDS(IC)
   10 XL=SQRT((X(1)-X(2))**2+(Y(1)-Y(2))**2)
      B(1)=B(1)+CTR*(X(1)+X(2))*XL/4.0
      B(2)=B(2)+CTR*(X(1)+X(2))*XL/4.0
      RETURN
   20 XL=SQRT((X(2)-X(3))**2+(Y(2)-Y(3))**2)
      B(2)=B(2)+CTR*(X(2)+X(3))*XL/4.0
      B(3)=B(3)+CTR*(X(2)+X(3))*XL/4.0
      RETURN
   30 XL=SQRT((X(1)-X(3))**2+(Y(1)-Y(3))**2)
      B(1)=B(1)+CTR*(X(1)+X(3))*XL/4.0
      B(3)=B(3)+CTR*(X(1)+X(3))*XL/4.0
C
      RETURN
      END
```

```
      SUBROUTINE FORCE
C
C*********************************************************************
C                      COMMON DATA BLOCK                             *
C*********************************************************************
      COMMON/SHAPE/X(3000),Y(3000),IV(6000,3),NOPTL,NOTR,NBW
      COMMON/LOCAL/XP(3),YP(3),SML(3,3),BL(3)
      COMMON/OUT/B(3000),S(3000,50)
      COMMON/DIRIC/DIR(3000),DC(6000)
      COMMON/CDEN/ICDS(6000),CDIST(6000),CD(6000)
C*********************************************************************
C
C            FORCE DIRICHLET BOUNDARY CONDITIONS
C
      DO10 I=1,NOPTL
C
C            CHECK FOR DIRICHLET CONDITION SET
C
      IF(DIR(I).GT.1.0E36) GOTO10
C
C            LOCATE THE ITH ROW AND COLUMN OF THE GLOBAL
C            A MATRIX WHICH IS IN RECTANGULAR FORM
C
      DO20 IJ=2,NBW
      J=NBW-IJ+2
      IZX=I+J-1
      IZZ=I-J+1
      IF(IZZ.LE.0) GOTO30
C
C            ADD CONTRIBUTION FROM DIRICHLET CONDITION TO
C            THE B VECTOR (ITH COLUMN)
C
      B(IZZ)=B(IZZ)-S(IZZ,J)*DIR(I)
C
C            DELETE ITH COLUMN
C
      S(IZZ,J)=0.0
   30 IF(IZX.GT.NOPTL) GOTO40
C
C            ADD CONTRIBUTION FROM DIRICHLET CONDITION TO
C            THE B VECTOR (ITH ROW)
C
      B(IZX)=B(IZX)-S(I,J)*DIR(I)
C
C            DELETE ITH ROW
C
   40 S(I,J)=0.0
C
   20 CONTINUE
C
C            SET THE (I,I) LOCATION OF THE A ARRAY TO 1.0
C
      S(I,1)=1.0
C
C            SET THE ITH ENTRY OF B VECTOR TO DIRICHLET VALUE
C
      B(I)=DIR(I)
C
   10 CONTINUE
C
      RETURN
      END
```

```
      SUBROUTINE SOLVE
C
C*********************************************************************
C                       COMMON DATA BLOCK                           *
C*********************************************************************
      COMMON/SHAPE/X(3000),Y(3000),IV(6000,3),NOPTL,NOTR,NBW
      COMMON/LOCAL/XP(3),YP(3),SML(3,3),BL(3)
      COMMON/OUT/B(3000),S(3000,50)
      COMMON/DIRIC/DIR(3000),DC(6000)
      COMMON/CDEN/ICDS(6000),CDIST(6000),CD(6000)
C*********************************************************************
C
C          DECOMPOSITION OF STIFFNESS MATRIX
C
      NP1=NOPTL-1
      DO1 I=1,NP1
      MJ=I+NBW-1
      IF(MJ.GT.NOPTL) MJ=NOPTL
      NJ=I+1
      MK=NBW
      IF((NOPTL-I+1).LT.NBW) MK=NOPTL-I+1
      ND=0
      DO2 J=NJ,MJ
      MK=MK-1
      ND=ND+1
      NL=ND+1
      DO2 K=1,MK
      NK=ND+K
    2 S(J,K)=S(J,K)-S(I,NL)*S(I,NK)/S(I,1)
    1 CONTINUE
C
C          SOLUTION OF SYSTEM OF EQUATIONS
C
      JM=1
      DO11 I=1,NP1
      MJ=I+NBW-1
      IF(MJ.GT.NOPTL) MP=NOPTL
      NJ=I+1
      L=1
      DO11 J=NJ,MJ
      L=L+1
   11 B(J)=B(J)-S(I,L)*B(I)/S(I,1)
      B(NOPTL)=B(NOPTL)/S(NOPTL,1)
      DO12 K=1,NP1
      I=NOPTL-K
      MJ=NBW
      IF((I+NBW-1).GT.NOPTL) MJ=NOPTL-I+1
      SUM=0.0
      DO13 J=2,MJ
      N=I+J-1
   13 SUM=SUM+S(I,J)*B(N)
   12 B(I)=(B(I)-SUM)/S(I,1)
      RETURN
      END
```

APPENDIX D
Other Methods

D1 BOUNDARY INTEGRAL METHOD

The boundary integral method is amongst the most recently developed
numerical methods for the solution of electrical field problems.
Although mathematically complex, at first glance, it is a very
attractive method for application to a broad range of problems.

In a general sense, the method assumes a solution which satisfies
the governing equations in the domain but which has unknown
coefficients. These coefficients are then determined by enforcing
the boundary conditions at a number of discrete points or subregions.
As a result, the computational effort, although lengthy, requires
little storage space as only the boundary points affect the solution.

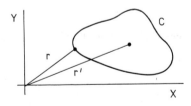

Figure D1

Consider the region shown above in figure D1, subject to Laplace's
equation with the boundary condition given in equation D.1.

$$\frac{\partial^2 \phi}{\partial x^2} + \frac{\partial^2 \phi}{\partial y^2} = 0 \qquad\qquad \phi(s) = g(s) \quad \text{on } C \qquad\qquad (D.1)$$

Letting σ denote a charge density on C, the potential ϕ at any point r within C is given by

$$\phi(r) = \frac{1}{2\pi\varepsilon_o} \int_c \sigma(r') \, \ell n \, \frac{1}{|r-r'|} \, dS' \qquad\qquad (D.2)$$

Approximating C by N straight line segments $\delta C_1, \ldots \delta C_N$ and using a step approximation to σ, we have

$$\sigma \cong \sum_i \sigma_i \, p_i(r)$$

where $\qquad p_i(r) = \begin{cases} 1 & \text{on } \delta C_i \\ 0 & \text{elsewhere} \end{cases} \qquad\qquad (D.3)$

Substituting (D.3) into (D.2) gives

$$\phi(r) \cong \sum_{i=1}^{n} \sigma_i \, \psi_i(r)$$

where

$$\psi_i(r) = \frac{1}{2\pi\varepsilon_o} \int_{\delta C_i} \ell n \, \frac{1}{|r-r'|} \, dS' \qquad\qquad (D.4)$$

Applying the boundary condition stated at, for example, each mid-point $\hat{r}_i$ of the δC_i, gives

$$\sum_{i=1}^{N} \sigma_i \, \ell_{ij} = g(\hat{r}_j) \qquad\qquad j = 1, \ldots N \qquad\qquad (D.5)$$

i.e. $\bar{L}\,\bar{\sigma} = \bar{g}.$

from which $\bar{\sigma}$ may be obtained. The potential at any point with C may now be obtained by substituting $\bar{\sigma}$ into (D.4).

This method may readily be extended to solve Poisson's equation with homogeneous space charge. The downfall of the method, is that non-uniform space charge poses problems. For any bounded region to be considered, the distribution of space charge must be homogeneous. It is fair to say that a piecewise distribution may be assumed, with each discrete region bounded and each boundary subdivided. This approach,although valid, loses the advantage gained from the small storage requirement of the method, by increasing the problem size dramatically.

D2 MONTE CARLO METHODS

The Monte Carlo method may be used to solve Laplace's or Poisson's equation in a closed region. The method is based on the mean value theorem of potential theory as stated in equation

$$\phi(r) = \frac{1}{4\pi a^2} \int_s \phi(r')dS' \qquad (D.6)$$

This states that the potential $\phi(r)$, at the centre of any sphere of radius a, within a region governed by Laplace's equation, is equal to the average value of the potential taken over its surface.

The significance of this, in terms of the evaluation of potential at a given point, lies in the fact that by constructing a series of random walks, each starting at the point of interest, and finishing at, or arbitrarily near to, the boundary, a statistical estimate of the potential at the point of interest $\phi(r_o)$ is given by

$$\phi(r_o) = \frac{1}{n} \sum_{j=1}^{n} \phi(r_j) \qquad (D.7)$$

where $\phi(r_j)$ is the potential at the finishing point of the jth random walk.

The method is thus inherently extremely simple. It is,however, extremely inefficient, in that a large amount of computational effort is required to find each potential value with most of the information implicit to each walk being discarded. Nonetheless, for problems involving Laplace's equation where only a small number of solution points are required, the method is easy to program and gives an accurate and rapid solution.

Subject Index

128

Author Index